11+

MATHS

Book Three

Stephen C. Curran

This book belongs to:

....

_____

Accelerated Education Publications Ltd.

Contents

Chapter Nine
PERCENTAGES
1. What is a Percentage?

Percentage is part of a whole. One hundred per cent is the whole, so a **Percentage is part of a 100**.

It is indicated by this sign.   **%**

Large and complex numbers can be reduced to parts of a hundred to make them easier to understand.
We see Percentages displayed in shops, banks, on advertisements and they are used for tax purposes.

Examples:

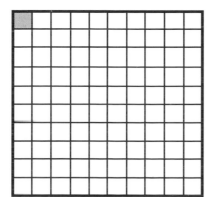

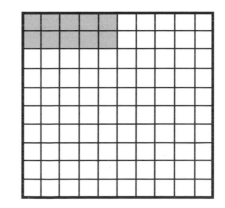

Percentages can be shown on a **Grid** of 100 squares.

1%	10%
1 part of a hundred	10 parts of a hundred

Exercise 9: 1

Count the Squares and write the **%** shaded in the space.

1)

........%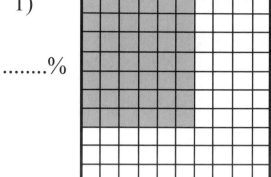

2)

........%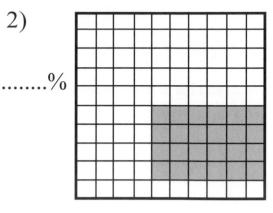

3)

........%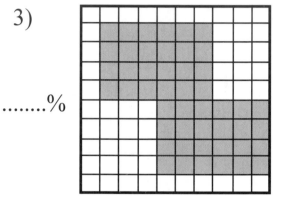

4)

........%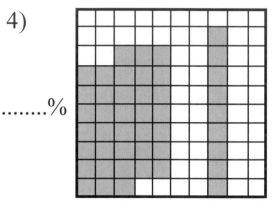

Shade in the Percentages shown below:

5)

32%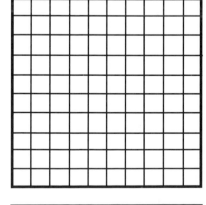

6)

23%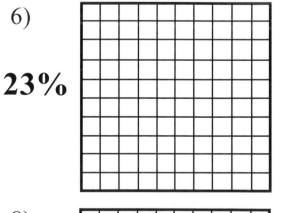

7)

12%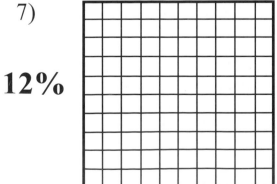

8)

55%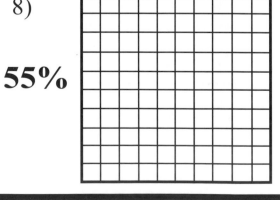

9) A boy called Simon Cooper was asked to shade his initials on a Grid of **100** Squares.

What Percentage do they take up on the Grid? ....%

10) Shade in the initials of your name on the Grid below:

What Percentage of the Grid do your initials take up?

.... %

Score Out of Ten →

$$\frac{5}{5} = 1$$

2. Percentages and Fractions

A Percentage can be **Expressed as a Fraction**:

Examples:

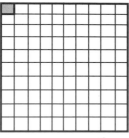

$$1\% = \frac{1}{100}$$

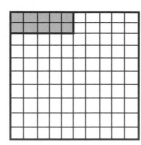

$$10\% = \frac{1}{10}$$ $\frac{10}{100}$ $\frac{1}{10}$

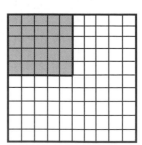

$$25\% = \frac{1}{4}$$ $\frac{25}{100} = \frac{1}{4}$

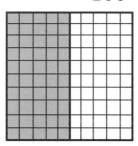

$$50\% = \frac{1}{2}$$

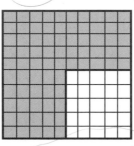

$$75\% = \frac{3}{4}$$ $\frac{75}{100}$

$$100\% = 1 \text{ Whole}$$ $\frac{100}{100} = 1$

a. Changing Percentages to Fractions

(i). Ordinary Percentage to Fraction

Example: | Convert **70%** to a Fraction.

70 hundredths
(70 parts of a 100)

Divide by 10 (Simplify)

$$70 \div 100$$

Divide by 10

$$\frac{70}{100} = \frac{7}{10}$$

Therefore   **70%** $= \dfrac{7}{10}$

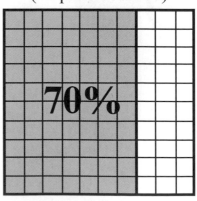

70%

Exercise 9: 2

Score [ ]

Change from % to Fraction:

1) **24%**

Simplify

$$\frac{24}{100} \quad \frac{12}{50}$$

$$= \frac{6}{25}$$

2) **80%**

Simplify

$$\frac{80}{100} \quad \frac{8}{10} \quad \frac{4}{5}$$

$$= \frac{4}{5}$$

3) **35%**

Simplify

$$\frac{35}{100} \quad \frac{7}{20}$$

$$= \frac{7}{20}$$

4) **95%**

Simplify

$$\frac{95}{100} \quad \frac{19}{20}$$

$$= \frac{9}{20}$$

5)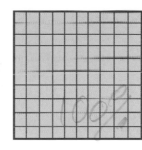

$$\frac{60}{100} \quad \frac{6}{10} \quad \frac{3}{5}$$

$$= \frac{3}{5}$$

6)

$$\frac{100}{100}$$

$$= \frac{100}{100} \quad 1$$

7) **16%** $= \frac{16}{100} \quad \frac{8}{50} \quad \frac{4}{25}$ 8) **40%** $= \frac{40}{100} \quad \frac{4}{10} \quad \frac{2}{5}$

9) **39%** $= \frac{39}{100}$ 10) **72%** $= \frac{72}{100} \quad \frac{36}{50} \quad \frac{18}{25}$

(ii). Whole Number Percentage to Mixed Number

Percentages bigger than a Whole One have more than one hundred parts. It can be represented diagramatically.

Example:

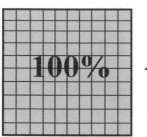

100% + **25%** = **125%**

7

Whole Number % to Mixed Number.

Example: Convert **275%** to a Mixed Number.

 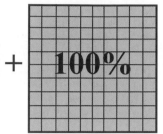 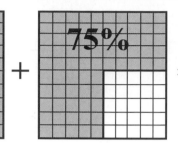 = **275%**

1. Write as a Fraction of 100.

$$\frac{275}{100}$$

2. Simplify (Divide).

Divide by 25

$$\frac{275^{11}}{100_{4}} = \frac{11}{4}$$

3. This is an Improper Fraction.

$$\frac{11}{4} \uparrow \text{Divide} = 2\frac{3}{4}$$

Therefore **275% = $2\frac{3}{4}$**

Exercise 9: 3

Change from Whole Number % to Mixed Numbers:

1)
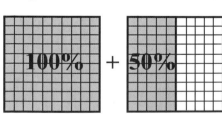

= 150% = $\dfrac{150^{3}}{100_{2}}$

= $\dfrac{3}{2} \uparrow$ Divide

= ....

2)
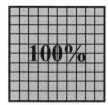

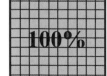 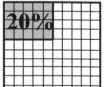

= 320% = $\dfrac{320}{100}$

= ....

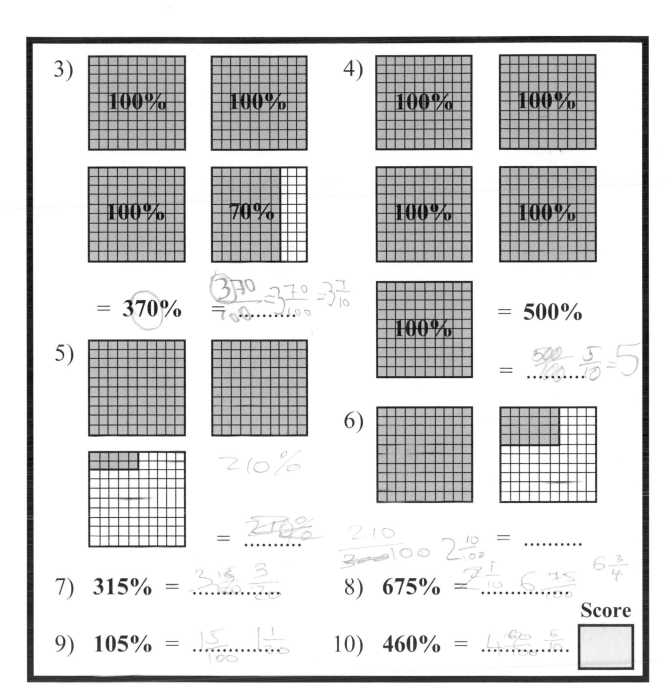

3) = **370%** $\frac{370}{100} = 3\frac{70}{100} = 3\frac{7}{10}$

4) = **500%** $= \frac{500}{100} \ \frac{5}{10} = 5$

5) 210%

= $\frac{210}{100}$ $2\frac{10}{100}$ = ...

6) = ...

7) **315%** = $3\frac{15}{100}$ $\frac{3}{20}$

8) **675%** = $\frac{210}{100}$ $2\frac{1}{10}$ $6\frac{75}{100}$ $6\frac{3}{4}$

9) **105%** = $\frac{15}{100}$ $1\frac{1}{20}$

10) **460%** = $4\frac{80}{100}$ $\frac{6}{10}$

Score

(iii). Mixed Number Percentage to Fraction

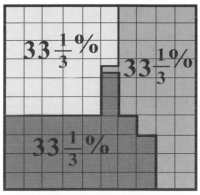

Percentages containing a **Whole Number and a Fraction** can be termed **Mixed Number or Fractional Percentages**.

The Grid has been Divided into **3** main sections. Each section has **33** and $\frac{1}{3}$ parts shaded.

Each shaded part of this Grid is

$33\frac{1}{3}$% or $\frac{1}{3}$ of the whole.

Mixed Number or Fractional Percentages occur because many numbers will not Divide exactly into 100.

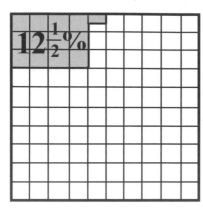

Example: $\boxed{12\tfrac{1}{2}\% \text{ as a Fraction.}}$

This Percentage cannot be made into a Fraction in its present form.

$$\frac{12\tfrac{1}{2}\%}{100}$$

It will not Simplify, as it is a Fraction of a Fraction.

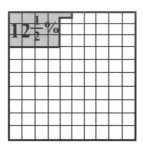 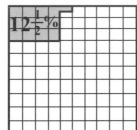

There are **25** Squares shaded.
There are **200** Squares in total.

If the whole Fraction is **Multiplied by 2**, the half is eliminated.

$$\frac{12\tfrac{1}{2}\% \times 2}{100 \quad \times 2}$$

Simplify $\dfrac{\cancel{25}^{\,1}}{\cancel{200}_{\,8}} \qquad \dfrac{1}{8}$

Therefore $12\tfrac{1}{2}\% = \dfrac{1}{8}$

Mixed Number % to Fraction.

(This method achieves the same as the above and is easier to remember).

1. **Convert** to an **Improper Fraction.** $12\tfrac{1}{2}\% = \dfrac{25}{2}$

2. **Multiply** the **Denominator by 100.** $\dfrac{25}{2 \times 100} = \dfrac{25}{200}$

3. **Simplify** the Fraction. Divide by 25 $\dfrac{\cancel{25}^{\,1}}{\cancel{200}_{\,8}} = \dfrac{1}{8}$

Exercise 9: 4

Change the Mixed Number % to a Fraction:

1) $3\frac{1}{3}\%$ = ...

2) $37\frac{1}{2}\%$ = ...

3) $66\frac{2}{3}\%$ = ...

4) $16\frac{2}{3}\%$ = ...

5) $87\frac{1}{2}\%$ = ...

6) $6\frac{1}{4}\%$ = ...

7) $62\frac{1}{2}\%$ = ...

8) $8\frac{1}{3}\%$ = ...

9) $83\frac{1}{3}\%$ = ...

10) $6\frac{2}{3}\%$ = ...

b. Changing Fractions to Percentages

(i). Fraction to Ordinary Percentage

Example: | Change $\frac{7}{10}$ into a Percentage.

Multiply by 100 (Cancel).

$$\frac{7}{10} \times 100$$

$$\frac{7}{\cancel{10}^1} \times \frac{\cancel{100}^{10}}{1} = \frac{70}{1}$$

Divide by 10

Divide by 10

Therefore $\frac{7}{10}$ = **70%**

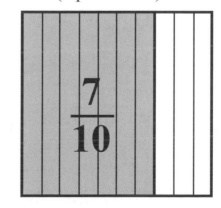

7 tenths
(7 parts of 10)

$\frac{7}{10}$

11

Exercise 9: 5

Change from Fraction to %:

1) 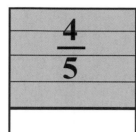 Cancel

$$\frac{4}{5} \times \frac{100}{1}$$

= ....%

2) 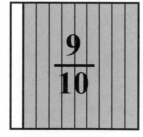 Cancel

$$\frac{9}{10} \times \frac{100}{1}$$

= ....%

3) 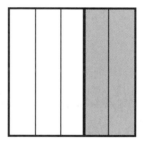 Cancel

= ....%

4) 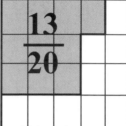 Cancel

= ....%

5)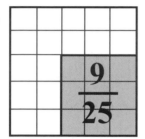

= ....%

6)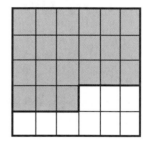

= ....%

7) $\frac{19}{20}$ = ...%   8) $\frac{9}{50}$ = ...%

9) $\frac{9}{30}$ = ...%   10) $\frac{17}{25}$ = ...%

(ii). Mixed Number to Percentage

A Whole One and a Fraction is a Mixed Number and can be Converted to a Percentage.

Example:

Show $1\frac{1}{4}$ as a diagram.

$$1 \text{ Whole} + \frac{1}{4} = 1\frac{1}{4}$$

12

Mixed Number to %.

Example: $2\frac{3}{4}$ as a Percentage.

$$\boxed{\begin{array}{c}1\\ \textbf{Whole}\end{array}} + \boxed{\begin{array}{c}1\\ \textbf{Whole}\end{array}} + \boxed{\frac{3}{4}} = 2\frac{3}{4}$$

1. **Convert** to an Improper Fraction. $2\frac{3}{4} = \frac{11}{4}$

2. **Multiply by 100** (Cancel).

   Divide by 4

   $\frac{11}{\cancel{4}_1} \times \frac{\cancel{100}^{25}}{1}$

Therefore $2\frac{3}{4} = \textbf{275\%}$

Exercise 9: 6

Change from Mixed Number to %:

1)

$$\boxed{\begin{array}{c}1\\ \textbf{Whole}\end{array}} + \boxed{}$$

$= 1\frac{3}{5}$

$= \frac{8}{5} \times \frac{100}{1}$

$= \ldots\ldots\ldots\%$

2)

$$\boxed{\begin{array}{c}1\\ \textbf{Whole}\end{array}} \quad \boxed{\begin{array}{c}1\\ \textbf{Whole}\end{array}}$$

$$\boxed{\begin{array}{c}1\\ \textbf{Whole}\end{array}} \quad \boxed{\frac{7}{10}}$$

$= 3\frac{7}{10}$

$= \ldots\ldots\ldots\%$

3)

1 Whole	1 Whole
1 Whole	1 Whole

[half-shaded square] $= 4\frac{1}{2}$

$= ....\%$

4)

1 Whole	1 Whole
1 Whole	$\frac{9}{20}$ grid

$= ....\%$

5) [full shaded square] [grid partially shaded]

$= ....\%$

6) [two shaded squares] [square with one quarter shaded]

$= ....\%$

7) $1\frac{1}{20} = ...\%$

8) $1\frac{3}{25} = ...\%$

9) $3\frac{3}{10} = ...\%$

10) $2\frac{1}{5} = ...\%$

Score [ ]

(iii). Fraction to Mixed Number Percentage

Mixed Number Percentages will Convert to a Fraction.

The Grid has been Divided into **3** main sections. Each section has one third shaded.

Each shaded part of this Grid is

$\frac{1}{3}$ or $33\frac{1}{3}\%$ of the whole.

[grid showing three columns each labeled $\frac{1}{3}$]

14

Fraction to Mixed Number %.

Example: $\boxed{\dfrac{1}{8} \text{ as a Percentage.}}$

1. **Multiply by 100 (Cancel).**

Divide by 4

$$\frac{1}{\cancel{8}_{2}} \times \frac{\cancel{100}^{25}}{1} = \frac{25}{2}$$

2. This is an **Improper Fraction.**

$$\frac{25}{2} \uparrow \text{Divide} = 12\frac{1}{2}$$

Therefore $\dfrac{1}{8} = 12\frac{1}{2}\%$

Exercise 9: 7

Change from Fractions to Mixed Number %:

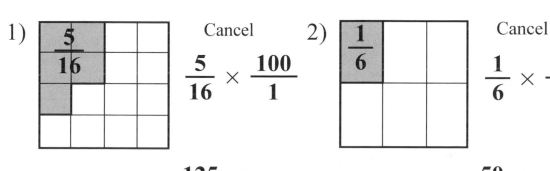

1) $\dfrac{5}{16}$

Cancel

$$\frac{5}{16} \times \frac{100}{1}$$

2) $\dfrac{1}{6}$

Cancel

$$\frac{1}{6} \times \frac{100}{1}$$

$$\frac{125}{4} \uparrow \text{Divide}$$

$$\frac{50}{3} \uparrow \text{Divide}$$

= ....%

= ....%

3) 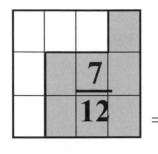 $\dfrac{7}{12}$ = ...%

4) 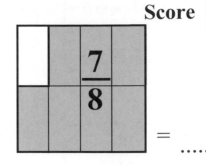 $\dfrac{7}{8}$ = ...%

5) 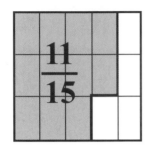 $\dfrac{11}{15}$ = ...%

6) $\dfrac{5}{6}$ = ...%

7) $\dfrac{1}{15}$ = ...%

8) $\dfrac{5}{12}$ = ...%

9) $\dfrac{3}{8}$ = ...%

10) $\dfrac{14}{15}$ = ...%

3. Percentage Calculations

The conversion of Percentages to Fractions and Fractions to Percentages is the basis of all Percentage Calculations.

| **% to Fraction** | Example: | Convert **80%** to a Fraction. |

Divide by 20 (Simplify) $\dfrac{\cancel{80}^{\,4}}{\cancel{100}_{\,5}} = \dfrac{4}{5}$

| **Fraction to %** | Example: | Change $\dfrac{4}{5}$ into a Percentage. |

Multiply by 100 (Cancel) $\dfrac{4}{\cancel{5}_{\,1}} \times \dfrac{\cancel{100}^{\,20}}{1} = 80\%$

16

Percentage to Fraction becomes **Percentage to Amount**.
Fraction to Percentage becomes **Amount to Percentage**.
All Percentage Calculations are of two types:

Either

Percentage to Amount   % $\longrightarrow$ Amount

A Percentage is given and an Amount has to be found.
There are 4 types of Question:

1. **Basic % to Amount** - e.g. Find **20%** of **£440**.

2. **Increasing Amount by %** - e.g. Increase **£55** by **32%**.

3. **Decreasing Amount by %** - e.g. Decrease **£60** by **40%**.

4. **Reverse % (Find an Original Amount** or **100%)** - e.g.
   If **65%** of a number is **260**, what is the whole amount?

Or

Amount to Percentage   Amount $\longrightarrow$ %

An Amount is given and a Percentage has to be found.
There are 3 types of Question:

1. **Basic Amount to %** - e.g. What % is **30** out of **200**?

2. **% Increase** - e.g. **£40** is increased to **£50** - % it increased.

3. **% Decrease** - e.g. **£80** is decreased to **£8** - % it decreased.

4. Percentage to Amount
a. Basic Percentage to Amount

a. Simple % calculations help find easy Percentages.

     10% - Find one tenth - **Divide by 10**.
     20% - Find one fifth - **Divide by 5**.
     25% - Find a quarter - **Divide by 4**.
     50% - Find a half   - **Divide by 2**.

Example: Find **25%** of **120**

To Find 25% is the same as finding one quarter.

Divide by 4   120 ÷ 4 = 30

25% of **120** = **30**

Other Percentages can be found in two or three stages.

Example: Find **35%** of **£250**

1. **Find 10% - Divide by 10**   £250 ÷ 10 = £25

2. **Find 30 % - Multiply by 3**   £25 × 3 = £75

3. **Find 35% - Add 5%**   £75 + £12.50 = £87.50

35% of **£250** = **£87.50**

Score

Exercise 9: 8 Find the following Amounts:

1) **40%** of **20** = ...

2) **20%** of **30** = ...

3) **85%** of **200** = ...

4) **90%** of **500** = ...

5) **25%** of **672** = ...

6) **30%** of **24g** = ... g

7) **65%** of **£2.60** = £ ....

8) **70%** of **£16** = £ ....

9) **75%** of **18m** = ... m

10) **60%** of **£9.50** = £ ....

---

b. Find an Amount from a %.

This is a standard technique for finding Percentages.

Example: Find **36%** of **250**.

Remember **of** is always ×

18

1. Write the **%** and **Amount** as a **Fraction**.

$$36\% = \frac{\overset{\%}{36}}{100}$$

$$250 = \frac{\overset{\text{Amount}}{250}}{1}$$

$$\% \longrightarrow \textbf{Amount}$$

2. **Multiply** (Cancel) the Amount by the Percentage.

$$\overset{\text{Divide by 50}}{\frac{36}{\cancel{100}^{2}}} \times \frac{\cancel{250}^{5}}{1}$$

3. **Simplify** the Fractions.

$$\overset{\text{Divide by 2}}{\frac{\cancel{36}^{18}}{\cancel{2}^{1}}} \times \frac{5}{1}$$

4. **Multiply out** the Fractions.

$$\frac{18}{1} \times \frac{5}{1}$$

$$36\% \text{ of } 250 = 90$$

Exercise 9: 9a   Find the Amount:

1) **30%** of **960p**.

   = £ ....

2) **80%** of **£625**.

   = £ ....

3) **12%** of **175cm**.

   = ... cm.

4) **26%** of **150km**.

   = ... km.

c. Find an Amount from a Whole Number %.

Example: | Find **125%** of **£52**. |

$$\% \longrightarrow \text{Amount}$$

Cancel, Simplify
and **Multiply out**.

$$\frac{125^{\,5}}{100_{\,1}} \times \frac{52^{\,13}}{1}$$

$$\mathbf{125\%} \quad = \quad \mathbf{£65}$$

Exercise 9: 9b   Find the Amount:

5) **204%** of **325g**.

6) **105%** of **£250**.

$$= \ \ldots\ldots\ldots \ \text{g.}$$

$$= \ £ \ \ldots\ldots\ldots$$

---

d. Find an Amount from a Mixed Number %.

Example: | Find $37\frac{1}{2}$**%** of **£80**. |

$$\% \longrightarrow \text{Amount}$$

1. **Convert Mixed Number %**
   into an **Improper Fraction**.

$$\frac{75}{2} \times \frac{80}{1}$$

2. **Multiply** the **Denominator**
   by **100**.

$$\frac{75}{2 \times 100} \times \frac{80}{1}$$

3. **Cancel, Simplify** and
   Multiply out.

$$\frac{75^{\,3}}{200_{\,1}} \times \frac{80^{\,10}}{1}$$

$$37\tfrac{1}{2}\% \text{ of } £80 \quad = \quad £30$$

Exercise 9: 9c Find the Amount: Score

7) $12\frac{1}{2}\%$ of **64p**.

= .... p.

8) $6\frac{1}{4}\%$ of **£80**.

= £ ....

9) $62\frac{1}{2}\%$ of **144cm**.

= .... cm.

10) $16\frac{2}{3}\%$ of **90km**.

= .... km.

b. Increasing Amounts by Percentage

Amounts can be Increased by a Percentage.

Method 1   Example: | **Increase £40 by 10%.** |

% ⟶ Amount

1. Find **10%** of **£40**.

$$\frac{\cancel{10}^{\,1}}{\cancel{100}_{\,10\;1}} \times \frac{\cancel{40}^{\,4}}{1}$$

10% of **£40** = **£4**

2. **Add** the Amount onto the Original Amount.

£40 + **£4** = **£44**

£40 Increased by **10%** = **£44**

Method 2

1. **Add** the **10%** on at the beginning.

100% + **10%** = **110%**

% ⟶ Amount

2. Find **110%** of **£40**.

$$\frac{\cancel{110}^{\,11}}{\cancel{100}_{\,10\;1}} \times \frac{^{4}\cancel{40}}{1}$$

£40 Increased by **10%** = **£44**

21

Exercise 9: 10a   What is the new Amount?

1) **Increase 90p** by **20%.**   2) **Increase £25** by **30%.**

= £ ....   = £ ....

Increase the following **Amounts** by **25%.**

3) **180cm**   4) **17.6km**   5) **420m**

= .... cm.   = ... km.   = ... m.

c. Decreasing Amounts by Percentage

Amounts can be Decreased by a Percentage.

Method 1   Example: **Decrease 150 by 5%.**

% $\longrightarrow$ Amount

1. Find **5%** of **150**.

$$\frac{5}{\cancel{100}^{2}} \times \frac{\cancel{150}^{3}}{1}$$

This is an **Improper Fraction.** $\frac{15}{2}$ $\uparrow$ Divide

$$15 \div 2 = 7.5$$

$$5\% \text{ of } 150 = 7.5$$

2. **Subtract** from
    the Original Amount. $150 - 7.5 = 142.5$

150 Decreased by **5% = 142.5**

22

Method 2

1. **Subtract** the **5%** at the beginning.

$$100\% - 5\% = 95\%$$

$$\% \longrightarrow \text{Amount}$$

2. Find **95%** of **150**.

$$\frac{\cancel{95}^{\,19}}{\cancel{100}_{\,20\,2}} \times \frac{\cancel{150}^{\,15}}{1}$$

This is an **Improper Fraction**.

$$\frac{285}{2} \quad \uparrow \text{ Divide}$$

150 Decreased by 5% = 142.5

Exercise 9: 10b   What is the new Amount?

6) **Decrease 60p** by **20%**.   7) **Decrease £40** by **30%**.

= .... p.   = £ ....

Decrease the following Amounts by 35%.

8) **120cm**   9) **20km**   10) **140m**

= .... cm.   = ... km.   = ... m.

---

d. Reverse Percentage

To find the Original Amount (100%) from a given Percentage.

Example: | **425** is **85%** of which Number? |

| **1%** of the number can be written as: | $\dfrac{425}{85}$ | Find the number. **Multiply** by 100% | $\dfrac{100}{1}$ |

It can be be Expressed as: $\%\ \longrightarrow\ \textbf{Amount}$

1. **Cancel** and **Simplify** the Fractions.

$$\frac{\cancel{100}^{20}}{1} \times \frac{\cancel{425}^{25}}{\cancel{85}^{\cancel{17}\ 1}}$$

2. **Multiply** out the Fractions. $25 \times 20 = 500$

The Original Amount is **500**.

Exercise 9: 11   Find the Original Amount (100%):

1) **150** is **60%** of which Number?

$\%\ \longrightarrow\ $ Am

$\dfrac{100}{1} \times \dfrac{150}{60}$ ....

2) What is the Whole Amount if **574** is **70%**?

$\%\ \longrightarrow\ $ Am

$\dfrac{100}{1} \times \dfrac{574}{70}$ ....

3) What is **100%**, if **45%** is **£108**? £ ....

4) If **55%** is **165km**, what is **100%**? .... km.

5) What is the Whole Amount if **190p** is **40%**? £ ....

6) What is the Whole Amount if **52cm** is **20%**? .... cm.

7) What is **100%**, if **65%** is **104m**? .... m.

8) If **30%** is **£21**, what is **100%**? £ ....

9) **56g** is **16%** of which Number? .... g.

10) What is **100%**, if **5%** is **3p**? .... p.

5. Amount to Percentage
a. Basic Amount to Percentage

a. Find a % from an Amount.

This involves Converting an Amount to a Percentage.

Example: $\boxed{\text{What Percentage of } \mathbf{220} \text{ is } \mathbf{44}?}$

1. Write the **Amount** and **%** as a **Fraction** and **Multiply**. (**Cancel**)

Amount	%
$\dfrac{44}{220}$	$\dfrac{100}{1}$

$$\text{Amount} \longrightarrow \% $$

$$\text{Divide by 20}$$

$$= \frac{44}{\cancel{220}^{11}} \times \frac{\cancel{100}^{5}}{1}$$

2. **Simplify** the Fractions.

$$\text{Divide by 11}$$

$$= \frac{\cancel{44}^{4}}{\cancel{11}^{1}} \times \frac{5}{1}$$

3. **Multiply out** the Fractions.

$$= \frac{4}{1} \times \frac{5}{1}$$

$$\mathbf{44} \text{ as a } \% \text{ of } \mathbf{220} = \mathbf{20\%}$$

Exercise 9: 12a   Find the ordinary %:

1) **150g** as a **%** of **1000g**.

= ....%

2) **85p** as a **%** of **£5**.

= ....%

3) **£90** as a **%** of **£250**.

= ....%

4) **42 m** as a **%** of **210m**.

= ....%

b. Find a Whole Number % from an Amount.

Example: | **£70 Compared** in **% terms** to **£40**. |

Amount $\longrightarrow$ **%**

Cancel, Simplify and **Multiply out**.

$$\frac{\overset{35}{\cancel{70}}}{\underset{1}{\cancel{40}}} \, {}_{2}\times \frac{\overset{5}{\cancel{100}}}{1}$$

$$£70 \;=\; 175\%$$

Exercise 9: 12b   Find the Whole Number %:

5) **112g Compared** as a **%** to **32g**

= ....%

6) **£62.50 Compared** as a **%** to **£25**

= ....%

---

c. Find a Mixed Number % from an Amount.

Example: | **£50** as a **%** of **£80**. |

Amount $\longrightarrow$ **%**

Cancel, Simplify and **Multiply out**.

$$\frac{\overset{25}{\cancel{50}}}{\underset{2}{\cancel{80}}} \, {}_{\cancel{4}}\times \frac{\overset{5}{\cancel{100}}}{1}$$

This is an **Improper Fraction**. $\quad \dfrac{125}{2} \uparrow = 62\frac{1}{2}\%$ Divide

$$£50 \text{ as a } \% \text{ of } £80 = 62\frac{1}{2}\%$$

26

Exercise 9: 12c Find the Mixed Number %:

7) **14m** as a **%** of **32m**.

= ....%

8) **60g** as a **%** of **144g**.

= ....%

9) **3km** as a **%** of **8km**.

= ....%

10) **£25** as a **%** of **£30**.

= ....%

b. Percentage Increase and Decrease

Finding out the Percentage an Amount has Increased by:

Example: £720 is Increased to **£828**. By what Percentage has it Increased?

1. Find out the **Difference** in Amount by Subtraction.

$$828 - 720 = 108$$

2. Express the new Amount as a Fraction of the Original Amount. $\dfrac{108}{720}$

3. Amount to % Calculation.

Amount ⟶ %

$$= \frac{\overset{3}{\cancel{108}}}{\underset{36\ \ 1}{\cancel{720}}} \times \frac{\overset{5}{\cancel{100}}}{1}$$

The **Percentage Increase** is **15%**.

A Percentage Decrease is done in exactly the same way.

Example: £500 is Decreased to **£375**. By what Percentage has it Decreased?

1. Subtract.

$$500 - 375 = 125$$

2. Calculation.

$$\frac{\overset{25}{\cancel{125}}}{\underset{5}{\cancel{500}}} \times \frac{\overset{1}{\cancel{100}}}{1}$$

The **Percentage Decrease** is **25%**.

Exercise 9: 13

Calculate the Percentage Increase or Decrease if:

40kg is <u>Increased</u> to: 1) **65kg** .... %   2) **72kg** .... %

£800 is <u>Decreased</u> to: 3) **£640** .... %   4) **£30** .... %

60kg is <u>Increased</u> to: 5) **78kg** .... %   6) **72kg** .... %

£120 is <u>Decreased</u> to: 7) **£96** .... %   8) **£90** .... %

£800 is <u>Decreased</u> to: 9) **£500** .... %   10) **£120** .... %

6. Mixed % Calculations

Exercise 9: 14   Calculate the following:

Percentage to Amount Questions.

1) **65%** of **£2.80**.

     = £ ....

2) **12%** of **350cm**.

     = ... cm

3) What is **$16\frac{2}{3}$%** of **270km**.

     = ... km.

4) **Increase £1.80p** by **45%**.

     = £ ....

5) **Decrease £2.20** by **30%**.

     = £ ....

6) What is the Whole Amount if **380km** is **40%**?

     = ... km

Amount to Percentage Questions

7) **£180** as a **%** of **£500**.   8) **3km** as a **%** of **24km**.

= ....%   = ...%

9) Give the **% Decrease** if 10) Give the **% Increase** if
   80km is reduced to **£50km**.   **£32** is increased to **£40**.

= ....%   = ...%

7. Profit and Loss
a. Finding an Original Cost Price

Finding an Original Cost Price from a Percentage Profit or Loss uses the same Calculation as a Reverse Percentage.

A. An Original Cost from a Percentage Profit.

Example 1:

> A shopkeeper sells a television for **£150**, making a **20%** Profit. What is the Original Cost Price of the television?

The Original Cost Price is always **100%** or $\dfrac{100}{1}$

The Selling Price is **£150**   Divide Amount $= \dfrac{150}{120}$
(**100% + 20% = 120%**)   by **%**.

It can be be Expressed as: **%** $\longrightarrow$ **Amount**

1. **Cancel** and **Simplify** the Fractions. $\dfrac{\cancel{100}^{5}}{1} \times \dfrac{\cancel{150}^{25}}{\cancel{120}_{1}^{\cancel{6}}}$

2. **Multiply** out the Fractions. $5 \times 25 = £125$

B. An Original Cost from a Percentage Loss.
Example 2:

> The same shopkeeper sells a table for **£63**, making a **30%** Loss. What is the Original Cost Price of the table?

The Original Cost Price is always **100%** or $\dfrac{100}{1}$

The Selling Price is **£63**
(**100% − 30% = 70%**)

Divide Amount by **%**. $= \dfrac{63}{70}$

It can be be Expressed as: **%** ⟶ **Amount**

1. **Cancel** and **Simplify** the Fractions.

$$\dfrac{\cancel{100}^{10}}{1} \times \dfrac{\cancel{63}^{9}}{\cancel{70}_{1}}$$

2. **Multiply** out the Fractions. $10 \times 9 = \textbf{£90}$

Exercise 9: 15a   Calculate the following:

1) A store sells a radio for **£156**. If the profit is **30%**, the Cost Price is £ ....

$$\begin{array}{cc} \% & \rightarrow \text{Am} \\ \dfrac{100}{1} & \times & \dfrac{156}{130} \end{array}$$

2) An art dealer sells a painting for **£3,500**, making a **40%** profit. How much did he originally pay it? £ ....

3) A girl buys **10** bottles of perfume, then sells them for **£2.40** each, making **60%** profit. What did she originally pay for the pack of **10** bottles? £ ....

4) A man sold his car for **£2,700** making a **20%** loss. The Original Cost was £ ....

$$\begin{array}{cc} \% & \rightarrow \text{Am} \\ \dfrac{100}{1} & \times & \dfrac{2,700}{80} \end{array}$$

5) A tailor makes a loss of **35%** by selling a suit for **£130**. What was the Original Cost Price? £ ....

b. Finding a % Profit or Loss

Percentage Profit/Gain or Loss makes use of exactly the same calculation as Percentage Increase or Decrease.

A. Finding a Percentage Profit (Appreciation).

Example: | Ben bought a computer game for **£12**. He sold it to a friend for **£15**. His % Profit was?

$$\textbf{Percentage Profit} = \frac{\textbf{Profit}}{\textbf{Original Amount}} \times \frac{\textbf{100}}{\textbf{1}}$$

The extra Amount Ben gained was: **£15 − £12 = £3**

$$\text{Amount} \longrightarrow \%$$

$$\frac{{}^{1}\cancel{3}}{{}_{1\,4}\cancel{12}} \times \frac{\cancel{100}^{\,25}}{1} = \overset{\%\ \textbf{Profit}}{\textbf{25\%}}$$

B. Finding a Percentage Loss (Depreciation).

Example: | Emily bought an **£8,000** car and sold it later for **£6,600**. Her % Loss was?

$$\textbf{Percentage Loss} = \frac{\textbf{Loss}}{\textbf{Original Amount}} \times \frac{\textbf{100}}{\textbf{1}}$$

The Amount Emily lost was: **£8,000 − £6,600 = £1,400**

$$\text{Amount} \longrightarrow \%$$

$$\frac{{}^{7}\cancel{1,400}}{{}_{2\,4\,8}\cancel{8,000}} \times \frac{\cancel{100}^{\,10\ 5}}{1} = \frac{35}{2} = \overset{\%\ \textbf{Loss}}{17\tfrac{1}{2}\%}$$

Exercise 9: 15b   Calculate the following:

6) What is the Percentage Profit if a computer is bought for **£625** and sold for **£725**. .... %

$$\text{Am} \longrightarrow \%$$
$$\frac{100}{625} \times \frac{100}{1}$$

7) A man buys a lamp for **£15** and sells it for **£18**. What is his Percentage Profit? .... %

8) A greengrocer buys **100** oranges for **£10** and sells them for **14p** each. His Percentage Profit is .... %

9) Nadia bought a ring for **£12.50** and sold it for **£10.25**. Her Percentage Loss was .... %

$$\text{Am} \rightarrow \% \\ \frac{225}{1250} \times \frac{100}{1}$$

10) Pavendeep bought a mountain bike for **£240** and sold it later for **£180**. What was the Percentage Loss? .... %

8. VAT (Value Added Tax)

Value Added Tax (VAT) is a Government Tax Added to various goods and services (exemptions include books and food). It is currently levied at **17.5%** and is charged at the point of sale of goods or services.

Total Cost of goods or services = **shop price + 17.5% VAT.**

a. Adding VAT to an Amount

Adding VAT (Value Added Tax) to an amount is the same as Increasing an Amount by a Percentage.

Example: A plumber costs a job at **£160** and Adds $17\frac{1}{2}$**%** **VAT**. How much does he charge the customer?

$$\% \rightarrow \text{Amount} \qquad \% \rightarrow \text{Amount}$$

$$\frac{117\frac{1}{2}}{100} \times \frac{160}{1} = \frac{^{47}235}{_{2}\cancel{200}_{10}} \times \frac{\cancel{160}^{8}}{1} = \frac{376}{2}$$

The plumber charges **£188 (inc. VAT).**

32

Exercise 9: 16a   Calculate the following:

1) A weekend break for a couple costs **£260** excluding VAT at **17.5%**. The total Cost for a couple is £ ....

$$\frac{\% \rightarrow \text{Am}}{} \quad \frac{117\frac{1}{2}}{100} \times \frac{260}{1}$$

2) An airline makes a **4%** surcharge (extra charge) on a holiday costing **£450** to cover extra fuel costs. Find the new price of the holiday. (treat the 4% surcharge in a similar way to an extra Tax like VAT). £ ....

b. Finding the cost without VAT

Finding the Cost without VAT uses the same calculation for finding a Reverse Percentage.

Example: A man buys a television for **£282** including VAT at **17.5%**. What is the Cost excluding VAT?

$$\frac{\%\rightarrow\text{Amount}}{} \quad \frac{100}{1} \times \frac{282}{117\frac{1}{2}} = \frac{\%\rightarrow\text{Amount}}{} \quad \frac{^{20}\cancel{100}}{1} \times \frac{\cancel{564}^{12}}{\cancel{235}^{47}\,1} = \mathbf{240}$$

The television costs **£240 (exc. VAT)**.

Exercise 9: 16b   Calculate the following:

3) A personal stereo costs **£94** including VAT at **17.5%**. The Cost without VAT is £ ....

$$\frac{\% \rightarrow \text{Am}}{} \quad \frac{100}{1} \times \frac{94}{117\frac{1}{2}}$$

4) A shop offers **5%** Discount on cash purchases. If a customer paid **£152** cash for some goods what was the Original Cost Price? (Use the Reverse % technique). £ ....

5) A woman saves **20%** in a sale and buys a coat for **£110**. What was the original price of the coat? £ ....

9. Two Percentages

It can be necessary to follow one Percentage by another.

Example: | A computer costs **£240** to manufacture. The factory wants **25%** Profit and VAT of **17.5%** must be added. Find the final price.

1. **% → Amount**

$$\dfrac{{}^{5}\cancel{125}}{{}_{1\!\!/\!4}\cancel{100}} \times \dfrac{\cancel{240}^{\,60}}{1}$$

$$= £300$$

2. **% → Amount**

$$\dfrac{117\frac{1}{2}}{{}_{1}\cancel{100}} \times \dfrac{\cancel{300}^{\,3}}{1}$$

$$= £352.50$$

If the final Amount is expressed as a Percentage it is **not** 25% + 17.5% = 42.5% but a **Percentage Increase**.

$$\textbf{Percentage Increase} = \dfrac{\textbf{Difference}}{\textbf{Original Amount}} \times \dfrac{\textbf{100}}{\textbf{1}}$$

The extra amount charged: **£352.50 − £240 = £112.50**

Amount → %   **Percentage Increase.**

$$\dfrac{112.5}{{}_{12}\cancel{240}} \times \dfrac{\cancel{100}^{\,5}}{1} = \mathbf{46.88\%}$$

Exercise 9: 16c Calculate the following: Score

6-8) A woman gets **10%** off the list price of a **£400** stereo in a sale. If she receives a further Discount of **5%** on the sale price for paying cash, what did she pay?

$$6) \quad \frac{\% \rightarrow Am}{100} \times \frac{400}{1} = £ \dots$$

$$7) \quad \frac{\% \rightarrow Am}{100} \times \frac{?}{1} = £ \dots$$

8) What is the overall Percentage Decrease?

$$\frac{Am \rightarrow \%}{400} \times \frac{100}{1} = \dots \%$$

A Gas engineer earns **£50** for a job. He receives a **10%** bonus from his firm, but pays **20%** Tax on the total.

9) He earns £ ....   10) The Tax payable is £ ....

10. Mixed Percentage Problems

All Problems make use of **only two types of Calculation**.

1. Percentage to Amount - Find an Amount from a %.

4 kinds of question
- Basic % to Amount.
- Increasing Amount by a %.
- Decreasing Amount by a %.
- Reverse % (Find Original Amount or 100%).

2. Amount to Percentage - Find a % from an Amount.

3 kinds of question
- Basic Amount to %.
- % Increase.
- % Decrease.

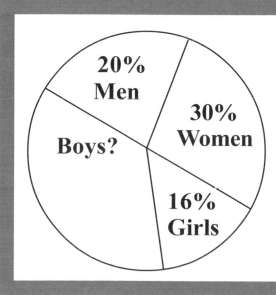

20% Men

30% Women

Boys?

16% Girls

Some questions have to be solved in stages. Example:

This Pie Chart shows the proportions of girls, boys, men and women that belong to a tennis club. There are **24** girls in the club. How many boys are there?

1. This is a **% to Amount** (How many boys are there?).

2. **Information Given** - Both halves of the Pie Chart are **50%**. **16%** represents **24** girls.

3. **Information Missing**.

    a. The % of boys - This can be found by Subtraction. $50\% - 16\% = 34\%$.

    b. Total Number of members in the club

    i. Find **1%** of the total.   ii. Find **100%**.

    Simplify   Divide by 2
    $\cancel{16\%} = \cancel{24}$ Girls   **Multiply**
    $\cancel{8\%} = \cancel{12}$ Girls $1\frac{1}{2} \times 100 = 150$
    $\cancel{4\%} = \cancel{6}$ Girls
    $\cancel{2\%} = \cancel{3}$ Girls   **100% = 150 People**
    $1\% = 1\frac{1}{2}$ **in the club**.

4. **Calculation**.

    $$\frac{\cancel{34}^{17}}{\cancel{100}_{\cancel{2}1}} \times \frac{\cancel{150}^{3}}{1} = 51$$

    There are 51 Boys in the Tennis Club.

Exercise 9: 17   Calculate the following:

1) A girl needs **60%** to pass an exam. If there are a possible **250** marks, how many must she score to pass? (% to Amount)

    She needs .... marks to pass.

    $$\% \rightarrow Am$$
    $$\frac{60}{100} \times \frac{250}{1}$$

2) A computer game usually costs **£65**. New versions of the game are made **20%** more expensive.
(Increase Amount by %)   % → Am

The new version of the game will cost £ .... $\dfrac{120}{100} \times \dfrac{65}{1}$

3) A hamburger meal normally costs **£3.80**, but the restaurant is offering **35%** off the normal price.
(Decrease Amount by %)

% → Am

$\dfrac{65}{100} \times \dfrac{380}{1}$ The meal will now cost £ ....

4) A boy gets **175** out of **250** marks in his maths exam.
(Amount to %)   Am → %

His Percentage will be .... %. $\dfrac{175}{250} \times \dfrac{100}{1}$

5) A music shop has a sale and reduces its prices on a number of items. A Percentage Reduction is given for each article with its sale price. What is the Original Price of each item? (Find the Original Amount - 100%)

Items	% Off	Sale Price	Original Price
a) Videos	15% off	£10.20	£ ....
b) Tapes	20% off	£2.00	£ ....
c) CDs	25% off	£10.50	£ ....
d) Records	35% off	£5.20	£ ....

Example: Question 5) a) Reverse %.   % → Am
Find the Percentage sale price first. $\dfrac{100}{1} \times \dfrac{1020}{85}$
100% − 15% = 85%

37

6) a) A boy saves **£320** for a CD player but it increases in price to **£400**. What is the Percentage Increase in price? (% Increase)

The Percentage Increase in price will be .... %.

$$\text{Am} \rightarrow \% \qquad \frac{80}{320} \times \frac{100}{1}$$

b) A year later the same boy sells his CD player that he bought for **£400** for **£250**. What did he lose as a Percentage? (% Decrease)

The Percentage loss (Decrease) will be .... %.

$$\text{Am} \rightarrow \% \qquad \frac{150}{400} \times \frac{100}{1}$$

7) There are **700** animals on a farm.
   a) How many hens are there?

   There are .... hens.

   b) How many pigs are there?

   There are .... pigs.

Pigs ? % | Cattle 26% | Hens 31% | Sheep 23%

8) Peter uses **7** of the ice cubes for drinks. What Percentage of the cubes are left?

There are .... % ice cubes left.

9) The new jeans Fiona wants have been reduced by **20%** in a sale. The original price was **£11.50**. How much is it now? The jeans will cost £ ....

10) Value Added Tax (VAT) is set at **$17\frac{1}{2}$%**. A TV set costs **£260**. What will the Cost be with VAT?
    The TV will cost £ ....

Score

11. Percentages and Decimals

Percentages are **parts of a 100** and Convert to Decimals.

Example: | Convert **37%** to a Decimal.

Put onto the **Decimal Table**.

Fraction

$$37\% = \frac{37}{100} \rightarrow$$

U	t	h	th
0 • 3	7		

a. Changing Percentages to Decimals

Example: | Convert **71%** to a Decimal.

Divide the Percentage by **100**.
Move the Decimal Point
two places to the left.

2 places left

$$71.0\% \longrightarrow 0.71$$

Exercise 9: 18a Convert % to Decimal.

1) **14%** = ...   2) **54%** = ...

3) **99%** = ...   4) **150%** = ...

5) **56%** = ...

b. Changing Decimals to Percentages

Example: | Convert **0.71** to a Percentage.

Multiply the Decimal by **100**.
Move the Decimal Point
two places to the right.

2 places right

$$0.71 \longrightarrow 71.0\%$$

Exercise 9: 18b   Convert Decimal to %:   Score

6) **0.94** = ...%   7) **1.25** = ...%

8) **0.05** = ...%   9) **2.65** = ...%

10) **0.11** = ...%

c. Percentage-Decimal Calculations

All Percentage calculations can be solved using Decimals.
If numbers do not cancel as Fractions, use Decimals instead.

(i). Percentage to Amount

A Percentage is given and an Amount has to be found.

Example: Find **36%** of **250**

1) **Divide 250 by 100.**
   (Move d.p. 2 places left) $250 \div 100 = 0.25$

2) **Multiply 0.25 by 36.**
   (Use Long Multiplication) $0.25 \times 36 = 90$

Exercise 9: 19   Find the following Amounts:

1) **24%** of **£85**
    = £ ....

2) **13%** of **140km**
    = ... km.

3) **16%** of **£224**
    = £ ....

4) **8%** of **30cm**
    = ... cm.

5) **72%** of **75 litres**
    = ... litres.

6) **15%** of **1.2km**
    = ... m.

7) **2.5%** of **£12**.

= .... p

8) **7.5%** of **40m**.

= .... m

9) **85%** of **660km**.

= .... km

10) **1.5%** of **£5**.

= .... p

(ii). Amount to Percentage

An Amount is given and a Percentage has to be found.

Example: What is **90** as a **%** of **250**?

1) **Divide 90 by 250**.
(Use Long Division)

$$90 \div 250 = 0.36$$

2) **Multiply 0.25 by 36**.
(Move d.p. 2 places right)

$$0.36 \times 100 = 36\%$$

Exercise 9: 20   Find the following Percentages:

1) **24** as a **%** of **64**.

= .... %

2) **£7** as a **%** of **£20**.

= .... %

3) **1200g** as a **%** of **3kg**.

= .... %

4) **98mm** as a **%** of **2.45m**.

= .... %

5) **35m** as a **%** of **56m**.

= .... %

6) **4mm** as a **%** of **3cm**.

= .... %

7) **3.64kg** as a **%** of **5.6kg**.

= .... %

8) **60cm** as a **%** of **4m**.

= .... %

9) **37mm** as a **%** of **148cm**.

= .... %

10) **45p** as a **%** of **£1.35**.

= .... %

12. Fractions, Decimals and Percentages

a. Useful Equivalents

Fraction	Decimal	Percentage	Fraction	Decimal	Percentage
$\frac{1}{2}$	0.5	50%	$\frac{1}{8}$	0.125	12.5%
$\frac{1}{3}$	$0.\dot{3}$	$33.\dot{3}\%$	$\frac{3}{8}$	0.375	37.5%
$\frac{2}{3}$	$0.\dot{6}$	$66.\dot{6}\%$	$\frac{5}{8}$	0.625	62.5%
$\frac{1}{4}$	0.25	25%	$\frac{7}{8}$	0.875	87.5%
$\frac{3}{4}$	0.75	75%	$\frac{1}{10}$	0.1	10%
$\frac{1}{5}$	0.2	20%	$\frac{1}{100}$	0.01	1%

b. Estimations

This involves Estimating Fractions, Percentages and Decimals as Proportions of one unit or a whole one.

Example: Estimate the Shaded portion as a Percentage, Decimal and a Fraction.

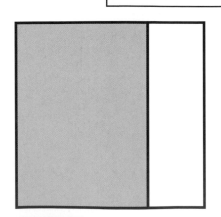

An Estimation that is within **5%** of the correct answer is acceptable.

This is Approximately:

70% or **0.7** or $\frac{7}{10}$

Exercise 9: 21

Estimate as a Fraction, Decimal and Percentage:

1)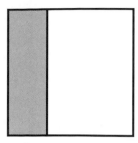

Fraction

= ....

Decimal

= ....

Percentage

= ....%

2)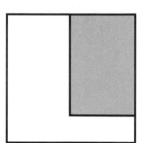

Fraction

= ....

Decimal

= ....

Percentage

= ....%

3)

= ....

= ....

= ....%

4)

= ....

= ....

= ....%

5)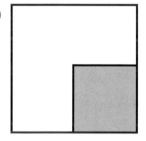

= ....

= ....

= ....%

6)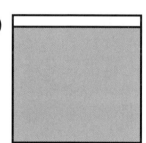

= ....

= ....

= ....%

7)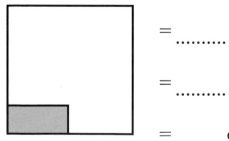

= ....

= ....

= ....%

8)

= ....

= ....

= ....%

9)

= ....

= ....

= ....%

10)

= ....

= ....

= ....%

c. Percentages, Decimals or Fractions

Ordering by Size (or Magnitude) can be done by changing the parts into either Fractions, Decimals or Percentages depending on what is most convenient.

Example:

> Put the following in Size order, smallest first.
>
> $\frac{3}{25}$ 13%   0.1   16% $\frac{4}{23}$

As there is no LCD it is best to change them to Decimals.

	$\frac{3}{25}$	13%	0.1	16%	$\frac{4}{23}$
	↓	↓	↓	↓	↓
1. **Convert** to Decimals.	0.12	0.13	0.1	0.16	0.174
	↓	↓	↓	↓	↓
2. **Add zeros** for comparison	0.120	0.130	0.100	0.160	0.174
3. **Re-order** the Decimals	0.100	0.120	0.130	0.160	0.174
	↓	↓	↓	↓	↓
4. **Convert** to original form	0.1	$\frac{3}{25}$	13%	16%	$\frac{4}{23}$

Exercise 9: 22   Find the following Amounts:

1) Put in Size Order, **smallest first**.   4% $\frac{3}{100}$ 0.02   = ...

2) Put in Size Order, **largest first**. $\frac{1}{13}$ 0.08   9%   = ...

Which is **smallest**?

3) 0.1 $\frac{2}{9}$ 2%   ....   4) $\frac{1}{8}$ 0.15   12%   ....

5) $\frac{1}{20}$ 0.06   4%   ....   6) 0.03 $\frac{3}{8}$ 4%   ....

Which is **largest?**   Score [   ]

7) **0.04** $\frac{3}{100}$ **5%**   .... 8) **7%** $\frac{1}{12}$ **0.06**   ....

9) $\frac{1}{30}$ **0.04** **2%**   .... 10) $\frac{1}{11}$ **9%** **0.1**   ....

d. Percentage Decimals/Fractions

Percentage Decimals are Percentages with a Decimal Point. Percentages are hundredths of a unit and this must be taken into account when converting a Decimal Percentage to a Normal Decimal.

Example: | Convert $4\frac{1}{4}$% into a Normal Decimal. |

Percentages are Fractions of a 100 (parts of a hundred).

The **4 units** of the **$4\frac{1}{4}$%** are **4 hundredths** : $\longrightarrow$ $\frac{4}{100}$

• Change $\frac{1}{4}$ into **0.25**.

U	t	h	th	t/th

• Divide **4.25** by **100**. **4.25%** $\longrightarrow$

U	t	h	th	t/th
0•0		4	2	5

(Move the Decimal Point 2 places left. If necessary, add zeros to the left of number, so the point can be moved.)

To Change Normal Decimals into Percentage Decimals reverse the process - Move Decimal Point 2 places right.

Exercise 9: 23 Write as Normal Decimals: Score [   ]

1) **2.13 %** = ... 2) **3.6 %** = ...

3) **0.7 %** = ... 4) **9.89 %** = ...

5) **$1\frac{4}{5}$%** = ... 6) **$10\frac{1}{2}$ %** = ...

Write as Percentage Decimals:

7) **0.334** = ... 8) **0.069** = ...

9) **0.812** = ... 10) **1.367** = ...

e. Ordering Percentage Decimals

It is important to be able to place Percentage Decimals and Normal Decimals in the correct Order of Magnitude (Size).

Example:

> **Which one of the following is the smallest?**
>
> $\dfrac{1}{25}$ **3.51%**   **0.05**   **3.6%** $\dfrac{1}{15}$

3.51%   3.6%   These two amounts have Decimal Points.
Note that Percentages are Fractions of 100.

The **3 units** of the **%** are **hundredths** :

$\dfrac{3}{100}$ Divide **3.51** by **100**   **3.51%** →
Move the Decimal Point 2 places left).

U	t	h	th	t/th
0·0		3	5	1

Convert the Fractions to Decimals (See **Book 2**).

1. **Convert** all the amounts to Decimals.

$\dfrac{1}{25}$	3.51%	0.05	3.6%	$\dfrac{1}{15}$
↓	↓	↓	↓	↓

2. **Add zeros** so it is easier to make comparisons.

0.04	0.0351	0.05	0.036	0.0666
↓	↓	↓	↓	↓
0.0400	0.0351	0.0500	0.0360	0.0666

3.51% is the smallest amount.

Exercise 9: 24   Which is **smallest**?   Score ☐

1) 0. 1 $\dfrac{3}{100}$ 2.15%   ....

2) $\dfrac{1}{8}$ 0.07   7.1%   ....

3) $\dfrac{1}{20}$ 0.06   9.9%   ....

4) 0.1 $\dfrac{3}{8}$ 1.95%   ....

Which is **largest**?

5) 0. 03 $\dfrac{1}{100}$ 4.16%   ....

6) 7.4% $\dfrac{1}{12}$ 0.06   ....

7) $\dfrac{1}{30}$ 0.61%   0.07   ....

8) $\dfrac{1}{11}$ 9.78%   0.1   ....

9) Put in size order, **smallest first**.   0.02 $\dfrac{3}{100}$ 2.1%   = ...

10) Put in size order, **largest first**. $\dfrac{1}{13}$ 0.08   9.1%   = ...

Chapter Ten
RATIO & PROPORTION
1. What is a Ratio?

A Ratio is a way of comparing quantities. One number can be evaluated as a Fraction or Percentage of another.

The quantities are separated by the sign as shown. **:**

The colon sign **:** means compared to.

Ratios are normally shown in the following way:

Example: 1 compared to 2   This is written as: **1 : 2**

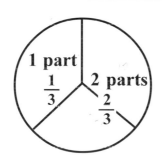

1 part
$\frac{1}{3}$ 2 parts
$\frac{2}{3}$

It can be represented Fractionally. There are three parts in total (add 1+2) meaning each part is one third.

1 part to to 2 parts.   or $\frac{1}{3}$ compared to $\frac{2}{3}$

This is called a **Unitary Ratio** because the relationship between the two quantities is based on a common unit.

Exercise 10: 1a

Write as a Unitary Ratio and represent Fractionally:

1a) Philip owns **4** CDs and Ann owns **5**.

....4.... : ....5....

$\frac{4}{9}$ to $\frac{5}{9}$

b) In class, **4** out of **11** pupils are boys, the others are girls.

....4.... : ....11....

$\frac{4}{15}$ to $\frac{11}{15}$

2a) **11** children keep mice,   b) **3** out of **7** girls like
     5 gerbils and **3** rabbits.   netball, the others don't.

.....3..... : .....5..... : .....11.....   .....3..... : .....7.....

.....$\frac{3}{19}$..... to .....$\frac{5}{19}$..... to .....$\frac{11}{19}$.....   .....$\frac{3}{10}$..... to .....$\frac{7}{10}$.....

2. Expressing Ratios as 1:n

Ratios can also be expressed in the form $\mathbf{1:n}$

Example: Express **3 : 4** in the form **1n**.

Divide both numbers by the first number.

1. **Divide** the first number by itself.

$$3 \div 3 = 1$$

2. **Divide** the second number by the first number.

$$4 \div 3 = 1.\dot{3} \text{ or } 1\tfrac{1}{3}$$

- -

Therefore **3 : 4** in the form **1:n**

Becomes $\mathbf{1 : 1.\dot{3}}$ or $\mathbf{1 : 1\tfrac{1}{3}}$

Exercise 10 : 1b   Write Ratio in form 1:n

3a) **2 : 3** ....   3b) **4 : 5** ....

4a) **2 : 7** ....   4b) **4 : 9** ....

5a) **12 : 20** .... (Cancel first)   5b) **15 : 30** ....

6a) **3 : 4.5** ....   6b) **2 : 2.5** ....

7a) **3 : 10.5** ....   7b) **2 : 9** ....

3. Ratios and Fractions

A Ratio can also be written as a Fraction if the two quantities are directly compared with each other.

Example: | Write **1 : 2** as a Fraction.

$$1 : 2 \ = \ \frac{1}{2} \quad \text{OR}$$

1 part   2 parts

Exercise 10 : 1c   Write the Ratio/Fraction:

8a) $\dfrac{4}{5}$ = ... : ....

b) **6 : 7** = ...

4. Ratios and Percentages

A Ratio can also be written as a Percentage.

Example: | Write **1 : 4** as a Percentage.

It can be shown diagramatically (See below).

$1 : 4$ One Part to four Parts or $\dfrac{1}{4}$

$\dfrac{1}{4} = \dfrac{25}{100}$ The Ratio is **25%**

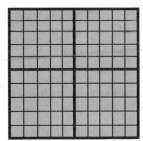

25 Parts   **100 Parts**

a. Ratio to Percentage

Example: | **2 : 5** as a Percentage would be:

1. Write the Ratio as a Fraction. $\dfrac{2}{5}$

2. Multiply by 100. $\dfrac{2}{{}_1\cancel{5}} \times \dfrac{\cancel{100}^{20}}{1}$

$$2 : 5 = 40\%$$

Exercise 10: 1d   Write the Percentage:

9a)   **3 : 4**

$$\frac{3}{4} \times \frac{100}{1}$$

b)   **9 : 20**   Do working here

=   ....%

=   ....%

b. Percentage to Ratio

Example: **40%** as a Ratio would be:

1. Convert to a Fraction.
$$\frac{40}{100}$$

2. Express as a Ratio. $\overset{4}{\cancel{40}} : \overset{10}{\cancel{100}}$

3. Simplify/Cancel. $\overset{2}{\cancel{4}} : \overset{5}{\cancel{10}}$

40% as a **Ratio** =   **2 : 5**

Exercise 10: 1e   Write the Ratio: Score ☐

10a)   **65%** $= \dfrac{65}{100}$ .... : ....   b)   **90%** .... : ....

5. Ratio and Proportion

Definitions:

A **Ratio** shows the relationship between two different Quantities.

A set of Quantities is in **Direct Proportion** to another set of Quantities when the use of a Constant Multiplier or Divisor results in an increase or decrease in one set that will match an increase or decrease in the other set.

Example: | Show that the set of Quantities **3, 5, 8** is in Direct Proportion to **12, 20, 32**.

$$3 \searrow \qquad \nearrow 12$$
$$5 \rightarrow \times 4 \rightarrow 20 \quad \text{or} \quad 5 \leftarrow \div 4 \leftarrow 20$$
$$8 \nearrow \qquad \searrow 32$$

$$3 \nwarrow \qquad \swarrow 12$$
$$8 \swarrow \qquad \nwarrow 32$$

The **Ratio** is used to compare the two sets of Quantities.

Example: | What is the Ratio between the two Quantities?

The **Ratio** is obtained by Simplifying **3** and **12**.

Divide both quantities by 3

$$\overset{1}{\cancel{3}} \quad \overset{4}{\cancel{12}}$$

$$1 : 4$$

Ratios represent Amounts. The size of the Ratio is in **Direct Proportion** to the Amounts (See Example below).

Philip and Jatinda Share a paper round in a Ratio of **1 : 2** for **18 weeks**. Philip does it **6 weeks** and Jatinda **12 weeks**.

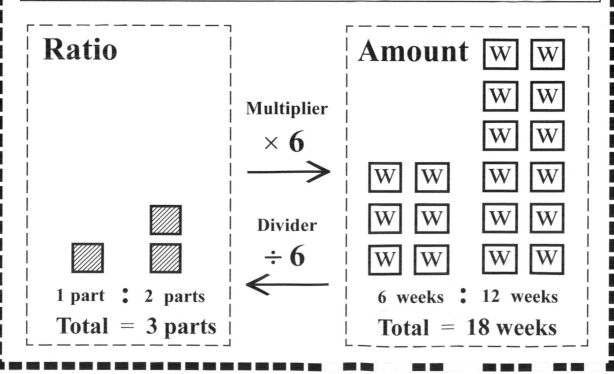

Ratio

1 part : 2 parts
Total = 3 parts

Multiplier
× 6 →

Divider
÷ 6 ←

Amount

6 weeks : 12 weeks
Total = 18 weeks

Ratio Boxes are a way of recording the information given and then calculating whatever is missing.

Total
18
Amounts
6 : 12
Multiplier/Divider
↑ ↑ × ÷ **6** × ÷ **6** ↓ ↓
Ratio
1 : 2

The Total number of weeks worked by both boys is 6 + 12 = **18 weeks**.

Philip has the paper round for **6 weeks**. Jatinda has the paper round for **12 weeks**.

The Ratio can be **Multiplied by 6** to find the Amounts or the Amounts can be **Divided by 6** to find the Ratio.

Philip and Jatinda share a paper round in the Ratio of **1 : 2**.

The same information can be recorded on a **Fraction Box**.

The Ratio of **1 : 2** can be converted to Fractions:

Fraction given	Fraction given
$\dfrac{1}{3}$	$\dfrac{2}{3}$
Amount 1 × 6 = 6 **6**	**Amount** 2 × 6 = 12 **12**
Total 6 + 12 = 18 **18**	**One Part** $\dfrac{1}{3} = 6$

(see **Book 2**).

Add the Ratio **1 : 2** (1 + 2 = 3). This means there are **3 parts**. The Ratio can be represented Fractionally as:

$\dfrac{1}{3}$ to $\dfrac{2}{3}$ is the same as: **1 : 2**

$\dfrac{1}{3}$ or **One Part** is equal to **6 weeks**

$\dfrac{1}{3}$ equals **6 weeks** (Philip) $\dfrac{2}{3}$ equals **12 weeks** (Jatinda)

The **Total** of **3 Parts** (6 + 12) is equal to **18 weeks**.

Ratio and Fraction Boxes express the same thing in different ways. Confusion is avoided by using Fraction Boxes to solve Fraction Problems and Ratio Boxes to solve Ratio Problems.

6. Amount to Ratio

This involves expressing the Ratio in its simplest form.

Example:

Express **45p** and **£1.20** as a Ratio in Lowest Terms.

1. Change to same units (pence).   The **Total** is not required.

2. Fill in the Ratio Box.

3. Simplify/Cancel.

$$\overset{3}{\cancel{\overset{\cancel{9}}{45}}} : \overset{8}{\cancel{\overset{\cancel{24}}{120}}}$$

Divide by 5, then by 3 (or 15).

$$3 : 8$$

Amounts
45 : 120
Divider
$\div 15 \ \div 15$
Ratio
3 : 8

The Ratio can also be expressed Fractionally as:

$$\frac{3}{11} \text{ to } \frac{8}{11} \quad \text{because } 3 + 8 = 11 \textbf{ Parts} \text{ in } \textbf{Total}.$$

Exercise 10: 2

Find the Ratio and the Fractional Representation for the Amounts:

1)   **£5 : £1.75**

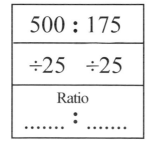

500 : 175
$\div 25 \quad \div 25$
Ratio .... : ....

$$\frac{20}{27} \text{ to}$$

Fractional
Representation

....

2)   **150cm : 3.5m**

150 : 350
.... : ....

to

....

53

3)   **400g : 1.6kg**

:
.... : ....

to

....

4)   **40cℓ : 1.2ℓ**

:
.... : ....

to

....

5)   **£36 : £54**

:
.... : ....

to

....

6)   **1.12m : 56cm**

:
.... : ....

to

....

Find the Ratio only for the following Amounts:

7) **20** girls in a class like orangeade, **6** like cola and **4** like lemonade. What is the Ratio?

:   :
.... : .... : ....

8) A club has **50** people. **30** are men, the others women. What is the Ratio?

:
.... : ....

9) **16** children have a cat, **12** children have a dog and **8** have a hamster. What will the Ratio of ownership be between the three kinds of animals?

:	:	
.... : .... :		

10) There are **27** horses. **9** are black, **3** are white and the others are brown. What is the Ratio between the three different colours of horses?

:	:	
.... : .... :		

When Ratios are represented as Fractions or Decimals it is necessary to convert them to Whole Numbers first.
An extended Ratio Box can demonstrate the various stages.

If the Ratio contains Decimals it must be Multiplied to convert everything to Whole Numbers.

Example 1: | Express **3 : 0.25** as a Ratio in Simplest form.

Multiply the Ratio by **4** to convert it all to Whole Numbers.

$$(4 \times 3) \quad (4 \times 0.25)$$

This will not simplify.

$$12 \quad : \quad 1$$

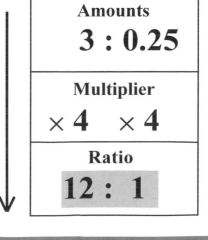

Amounts
3 : 0.25
Multiplier
×**4**   ×**4**
Ratio
12 : 1

Ratios can be in the form of Fractions which means they have to be Multiplied first to produce the simplest form.

Example 2: Express $\frac{2}{3} : \frac{4}{5}$ as a Ratio in Simplest form.

1. **Multiply** by the Lowest Common Multiple (LCM) of both Fractions.

$$\frac{2}{\cancel{3}} \times \frac{\cancel{15}^{5}}{1} \qquad \frac{4}{\cancel{5}} \times \frac{\cancel{15}^{3}}{1}$$

$$(2 \times 5) \qquad (3 \times 4)$$

$$\mathbf{10} \quad : \quad \mathbf{12}$$

2. **Divide** (Simplify) by Highest Common Factor (HCF).

Divide by 2   Divide by 2

$$\cancel{10}^{5} \quad : \quad \cancel{12}^{6}$$

$$\mathbf{5} \quad : \quad \mathbf{6}$$

Amounts
$\frac{2}{3} : \frac{4}{5}$
Multiplier $\times \mathbf{15} \times \mathbf{15}$
New Amounts   **10 : 12**
Divider $\div 2 \quad \div 2$
Ratio   **5 : 6**

Exercise 10: 3   Find the Ratio from the Amounts:

1) $\frac{5}{4} : \frac{5}{7}$

$\frac{5}{4} : \frac{5}{7}$
$\times 28 \ \times 28$
New Amounts
$\div 5 \quad \div 5$
Ratio   .... : ....

2) $6 : \frac{3}{5}$

$6 : \frac{4}{5}$
$\times 5 \quad \times 5$
.... : ....

3)   **5 : 0.3̇**

5 : 0.3̇
Multiplier × 3   × 3
Ratio .... : ....

4) $\frac{4}{5}$ **: 10**

$\frac{4}{5}$: 10
.... : ....

5) $\frac{5}{7}$ **: 5**

:
.... : ....

6)   **0.2 : 4**

0.2 : 4
.... : ....

7) $\frac{5}{6}$ **:** $\frac{5}{8}$ **:** $\frac{5}{12}$

$\frac{5}{6}$: $\frac{5}{8}$: $\frac{5}{12}$
.... : .... : ....

8)   **3 :** $\frac{3}{5}$

:
.... : ....

Score

9) $\frac{3}{4} : 3$

$\frac{3}{4} : 3$
.... : ....

10) $2\frac{2}{3} : 1\frac{1}{7}$

:
.... : ....

7. Ratio to Amount

There are three types of Ratio to Amount Question.
   a. Type 1 - (Ratio and Total given).
   b. Type 2 - (Ratio and Amount given).
   c. Type 3 - (Ratio and Multiplier given).
All three types can be solved with Ratio Box techniques.

a. Type 1 - (Ratio + Total given)

Example:

Sand and cement are mixed in a Ratio of **2 : 1**. How much sand and cement is there in a **450kg** mixture?

1. The **Information Given**.
   Ratio - **2 : 1**
   Total - **450kg**
2. Place the information into the **Ratio Box**.

Total
450kg
Amounts
? : ?
Multiplier
$\times$ **?** $\times$ **?**
Ratio
2 : 1

58

3. **Add** the Ratio.

$2 + 1 = 3$

4. **Divide** the Total by 3.

$450 \div 3 = 150$

5. **Multiply** the Ratio by the Multiplier.

$2 \times 150 = 300$

$1 \times 150 = 150$

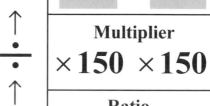

Total
450kg

Amounts	
300 : **150**

Multiplier	
$\times 150$	$\times 150$

Ratio
2 : 1

The mixture is **300kg** of **sand** and **150kg** of **cement**.

A shorthand way of remembering the method.

Learn the **Order of Operations**
A   D   M
$+ \rightarrow \div \rightarrow \times$

Exercise 10: 4a   Find the Amount:

1) **£120** is won in a draw. It is Divided in a Ratio of **5 : 7** between two winners. How much did they each receive?

£120
:
5 : 7

£ .... : £ ....

18m
:   :
1 : 2 : 3

2) A fishing line is **18m** long. Divide it in the Ratio of **1 : 2 : 3**

.... m : .... m : .... m

59

b. Type 2 - (Ratio + Amount given)

Example:

Billy and Lara save money on a weekly basis in the Ratio of **3 : 2**. If Billy saves **£15** a week, how much money does Lara save? How much money do they save altogether?

Total
?

Amounts
15 : ?

Multiplier
×?   ×?

Ratio
3 : 2

1. The **Information Given**.
   Ratio   - 3 : 2
   Amount - £15 (Billy)

2. Place in the information into the **Ratio Box**.

   The **Multiplier** has to be found.

3. **Divide** Amount by **3**.
   15 ÷ 3 = 5

4. **Multiply** the Ratio by the Multiplier.
   2 × 5 = 10

5. **Add** the Ratio.
   15 + 10 = 25

Total
£25

Amounts
15 : 10

Multiplier
×5   ×5

Ratio
3 : 2

$+$
↑
$×$
↑
$÷$

Lara saves **£10**. In Total they save **£25**.

Learn the **Order of Operations**
D   M   A
÷ → × → +

Exercise 10: 4b   Find the Amount:

3) A teacher's desk contains pens and pencils in the Ratio of **6 : 5**. There are **30** pens. How many pencils are there in the desk? ......60...... pencils.

30 : 25
6 : 5

4) Stephen and Janice share out some stickers in a Ratio that can be written fractionally as $\frac{2}{3}$ to $\frac{1}{3}$. Janice receives the larger Share of **30**. What Share does Stephen receive? .... stickers.

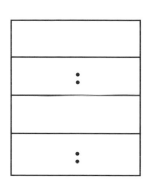

5) **5** out of every **8** girls in a class like playing netball. If **20** girls like playing netball, how many do not like playing? .... girls.

5 : 3
20 : 12

c. Type 3 - (Ratio + Multiplier given)

Example:

72 mints were Shared among **14** boys and **15** girls (**14 : 15**). If each boy received **3** mints, how many did each girl receive?

1. The **Information Given**.
   Ratio   -   14 : 15
   Multiplier -   × 3

2. Place the information into the **Ratio Box**.

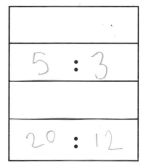

Total
72
Amounts
? : ?
Multiplier
× 3   ×?
Ratio
14 : 15

The **Other Multiplier** has to be found.

3. **Multiply** the Ratio by **3**.

   3 × 14 = 42

4. **Subtract** the Amount from the Total.

   72 − 42 = 30

5. **Divide** the Amount by the Ratio.

   30 ÷ 15 = 2

Total
72

Amounts
42 : 30

Multiplier
×3   ×2

Ratio
14 : 15

÷ ↑

— ↑

×

Each girl receives **2 mints**.

Learn the **Order of Operations**
M   S   D
× → − → ÷

Exercise 10: 4c Find the missing Multiplier:

6) The Ratio of wet days to dry days during a holiday is **5 : 3**. There were **2** times as many dry days. If the holiday lasted for **21** days, how many wet days were there?

21
:
× 2
5 : 3

.... wet days.

7) **77** yoyos are owned by one class of children. If **16** children have **2** yoyos each, how many do the other **15** children have each? (The 15 have the same number each).

:
:

.... yoyo(s).

62

d. Creating the Ratio

Some Ratio to Amount questions require the creation of the Ratio.

Example:

> Andy has **half as many** stickers as Billy and Chris has **one third as many** as Billy. Altogether they have **33** stickers. How many does each boy have?

1. **Find the Ratio**.

   Estimate an Amount Billy could have, as the other Amounts relate to his.

   Simplify
   Divide by 2

   Estimate Billy's Amount - $\cancel{12}$ ^{6} **6 Stickers**

   Andy has half as many - $\cancel{6}$ ^{3} **3 Stickers**

   Chris has one third as many - $\cancel{4}$ ^{2} **2 Stickers**

   This gives the **Ratio 6 : 3 : 2**

2. **Find the Amount**.

   · **Add** the Ratio.

     6 + 3 + 2 = 11

   · **Divide** the Total by 11 to find the Multiplier.

     33 ÷ 11 = 3

   · **Multiply** the Ratio by the Multiplier.

Total
33

Amounts		
18 :	**9** :	**6**

Multiplier		
× 3	× 3	× 3

Ratio		
6 :	**3** :	**2**

Billy has **18 stickers**, **Andy** has **9** and **Chris** has **6**.

Exercise 10: 4d Find the Amount: Score ☐

117	
:	:
:	:

8) The ages of Gran, Auntie and Sue Add up to **117**. Gran is **twice as old** as Auntie, who is **4 times** as old as Sue. What are their ages?

Gran ...... Auntie ...... Sue ......

9) An hour (**60 mins**) is Divided into **3 parts**. Part 1 is **twice as long** as Part 2, which is **3 times as long** as Part 3. How many minutes are in each part?

Part 1 ...... Part 2 ...... Part 3 ......

:	:
:	:

:	:
:	:

10) **104** sweets are Shared among **3** girls. Paula has **3 times as many** as Jane, who has **3 times as many** as Bavneep. How many does each girl have?

Paula ..... Jane ..... Bavneep .....

8. Other Ratio Types
a. Increasing & Decreasing by Ratio

In these type of questions it is necessary to establish the relationship between one unit and the larger amount.

Example: | **Seven men** take **28 days** to build a house. How long would it take **4 men**?

1. **Multiply** to find out how long it would take for **one man** to build the house. It would take seven times as long.

   $7 \times 28 = $ **196 days** for **one man** to build the house.

2. **Divide** to find out how long it would take **4 men** to build the house. $196 \div 4 = 49$ **days**

It would take **49 days** for **4 men** to build the house.

Exercise 10: 5a   Find the Amount:

1) If **8 children** can plant a garden with seeds in **10 hours** how long would it take **20 children** to do the same job? (Assume they work at the same speed) ....4..... hours.

----

2) If **5 people** were hired to clean an office building it would take **18 days**. How long would it take just **3 people** to do the same job? ....30..... days.

b. Unequal Shares

This type occurs when quantities are NOT Divided into equal parts or shares. Questions often contain the words 'greater than', 'more than', 'less than' or 'fewer than'. The first kind of question has **two Unequal Shares**:

Example: | In one season Arsenal and Chelsea scored a total of **190 goals**. Chelsea scored **40 goals** fewer than Arsenal. How many goals did each team score?

1. **Subtract** the difference between the two quantities from the total quantity. $190 - 40 = 150$ **goals**

2. **Divide** the answer by **2**. This gives the smaller amount.
    $150 \div 2 =$ **Chelsea scored 75 goals**

3. **Add** the difference in amounts to find the larger amount.
    $75 + 40 =$ **Arsenal scored 115 goals**

Note: Order of Operations is **Subtract ⟶ Divide ⟶ Add**

Exercise 10: 5b   Find the Amount:

3) Vidhur and Anne together have a total of **£10.60**. Vidhur has **£2.40** more than Anne. How much does each child have?

Subtract .... − .... = ...8.20...

Divide .... ÷ 2 = ...4.10... (Anne's share)

Add .... + ... = ...6.50... (Vidhur's share)

Vidhur has £ .... and Anne has £ ....

- -

4) The sum of two numbers is **420**. The difference between the two numbers is **60**. What are the two numbers?
The smaller number is ..180.... The bigger number is ..240...

360

180

- -

5) A piece of string **130cm** long is cut into two different lengths. One piece is **50cm** longer than the other. What is the length of each piece of string?
The short piece is ...50... cm. The long piece is ...80... cm.

80

Some questions involve repeating the process twice.
This second kind of question has **three Unequal Shares**:
Example:

Pauline and Katherine together have **£40** more than Julie. Pauline has **£8** more than Katherine. If they have **£480** altogether, how much do they each have?

| Stage One | - If Pauline and Katherine are grouped as one person it is then possible to work out how much Julie has.

1. **Subtract** the difference in amounts between Pauline/ Katherine and Julie (£40) from the whole amount (£480).

£480 − £40 = £440

2. **Divide** the answer by **2**. This gives the smaller amount.

£440 ÷ 2 = Julie's share is £220

3. **Add** the difference in amounts (£40) to Julie's share (£220) to find Pauline/Katherine's share (larger amount).

$$£220 + £40 = \text{Pauline/Katherine's share of } £260$$

Stage Two - Pauline and Katherine's share (£260) now has to be separated. The same stages now have to be repeated. Pauline has **£8** more than Katherine.

4. **Subtract** the difference in amounts between Pauline and Katherine (£8) from the whole amount (£260).

$$£260 - £8 = £252$$

5. **Divide** the answer by **2**. This gives the smaller amount.

$$£252 \div 2 = \text{Katherine's share of } £126$$

6. **Add** the difference in amounts (£8) to Katherine's share (£126) to find Pauline's share (larger amount).

$$£126 + £8 = \text{Pauline's share of } £134$$

Answer - The **£480** is shared out in the following ways:
Julie has **£220**; **Katherine** has **£126**; **Pauline** has **£134**

Note: Order of Operations **Subtract → Divide → Add**
was repeated twice over.   **Subtract → Divide → Add**

Exercise 10: 5c   Find the Amount:

6) Three boys did a sponsored walk and raised **£660** for a local charity. Alex and Dean raised **£240** more than John. Alex raised **£60** more than Dean. How much did they each raise?

Stage One - To find John's share treat Alex/Dean as one.

Subtract .... − .... = ...

Divide .... ÷ **2** = ... (John's share)

Add .... + ... = ... (Alex/Dean's share)

Stage Two - Now it is time to find Alex and Dean's share.

Subtract .... − .... = ...

Divide .... ÷ **2** = ... (Dean's share)

Add .... + ... = ... (Alex's share)

John raised £ .... **Alex** raised £ .... **Dean** raised £ ....

7) Daniel, Premdeep and Ravi altogether have collected **600** stamps. Daniel and Premdeep together have **120** more stamps than Ravi. Daniel has **48** stamps more than Premdeep. How many stamps does each child have?

Ravi has .... Daniel has .... Premdeep has ....

c. Double Shares

Some sharing questions have an amount that has been counted twice.   Example:

> Sam and Priya together have **£48**. Sam and Carl together have **£64**. Altogether the three children have **£84**. Work out how much each child has.

Notice that there are four amounts but only three children. Sam's amount has been counted twice.

1. **Add** the Sam/Priya (£48) and Sam/Carl (£64) amounts.
   £48 + £64 = **£112** (Sam's share has been counted twice)
2. **Subtract** the total amount (£84) from the above (£112)
   £112 − £84 = **£28** (This gives Sam's share)

Sam's share can now be used to find the other shares.

3. **Subtract** Sam's (£28) from Sam/Priya's (£48) amounts.
   £48 − £28 = **£20** (This gives Priya's share)
4. **Subtract** Sam's (£28) from Sam/Carl's (£64) amounts.
   £64 − £28 = **£36** (This gives Carl's share)

Answer - **Sam** has **£28**;   **Priya** has **£20**;   **Carl** has **£36**

Exercise 10: 5d   Find the Amount:

8) James and Keshav together have **92** swop cards. James and Andrew together have **72** swop cards. Altogether the three boys have **126** swop cards.

   a) Who has the least swop cards? ....

   b) Who has the most swop cards? ....

Keshav gives some of his swop cards to the other two boys, so they all have the same number (Divide total by 3).

   c) How many did he give to James? .... swop cards.

   d) How many did he give to Andrew? .... swop cards.

- -

9) Melanie buys **6** erasers and **8** pencils at a cost **£3.40** Julie buys **6** erasers and **4** pencils at a cost of **£2.60**. In all they spend **£6.00**. (clue - Find cost of 1 pencil & 1 eraser) Use this information to find the cost of:

a) **6** pencils £ ....   b) **3** erasers + **2** pencils £ ....

d. More Complex Ratio Problems

Some Ratio Box questions can seem more complicated: Example:

Vicky and Wendy collected **four times** as much waste paper as Betty. Vicky Collected **16kg** more than Wendy. Altogether they collected **240kg**. How much did each girl collect?

Total	**240**
Amounts	**192 : 48**
Multiplier	**×48 ×48**
Ratio	**4 : 1**

1. For a Ratio, group Vicky and Wendy:

   4 : 1

Vicky/Wendy Betty

This part of the question follows the standard Ratio Box format.

The **order of operations** is: $+ \rightarrow \div \rightarrow \times$

69

We now know that Betty collected **48kg** of paper.
We also know Vicky collected **16kg** more than Wendy.

2. **Divide** Wendy/Vicky's share by **2**   £192 ÷ 2 = £96

3. **Add/Subtract** to Wendy/Vicky's
shares to create a gap of **16kg**.
Add 8kg to Wendy's share;
Subtract 8kg from Vicky's share.

Vicky	Wendy
96kg	**96kg**
+8	− 8
104kg	**88kg**

Vicky has **104kg**: **Wendy** has **88kg**: **Betty** has **48kg**

Exercise 10: 5e   Find the Amount: Score

10) Paul, John and Don together have
252 stickers. John receives **6** from
Paul, and Don gives **4** to John. At
the end they discover that Paul has
twice as many as John and John
has twice as many as Don.

	:	:
	:	:

Create the Ratio and use the Ratio Box to find the final Amounts

a) At the finish Paul has .... John has .... Don has ....

Reverse what was given/taken to each to find the original Amounts

b) At the start Paul has .... John has .... Don has ....

---

9. Maps and Scale Drawings

Ratios are used for Maps and Scale
Drawings. The Ratio is in **Direct
Proportion** to the actual Distance
represented.
Example:

A map scale reads **1cm : 3km**. If a
distance on the map measures **5cm**,
the real distance will be **15km**.

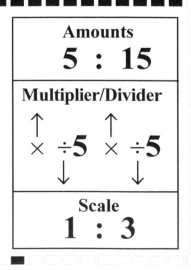

Amounts
5 : 15
Multiplier/Divider
↑   ↑
× ÷**5** × ÷**5**
↓   ↓
Scale
1 : 3

70

a. Amount to Scale

Example:

A school hall is **40m** long. If a Plan represents this as **8cm**, what is the Scale?

School Hall

← **40m** →

Amounts
8 : 40
Divider
?   ?
Scale
? : ?

1. Fill in the Ratio Box.

2. **Divide** the Amounts by a Factor of both Amounts.

    8 ÷ 8 = 1

    40 ÷ 8 = 5

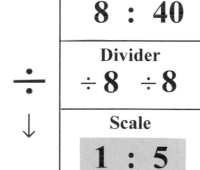

Amounts
8 : 40
Divider
÷8   ÷8
Scale
1 : 5

The **Scale** is **1cm : 5m**

Exercise 10: 6a   Write the Scale:

:
:

1) A Plan is drawn for a bird table. The bird table measures **20cm** on the Plan. What Scale has been used?

The Scale is ...... : ......

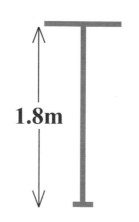
1.8m

2) A class of year 5 children do some orienteering. Their journey of **49.5km** measures **16.5cm** on the Map. What is the Scale of the Map? ...... **:** ......

| : |
| : |
| : |

| : |
| : |
| : |

3) A Scale drawing is made of a wardrobe. The Height of the wardrobe on the drawing measures **9cm** and the real Height is **180cm**. The Scale is ...... **:** ......

b. Scale to Amount

Example:

On a Plan a school hall is drawn at a Scale of **1cm** to **5m**. What is the real Length?

| School Hall |

← **8cm** →

Amounts
8 : ?
Multiplier
?   ?
Scale
1 : 5

1. Fill in the Ratio Box.

2. **Divide** the Amount by the Scale to find the Multiplier.
   8 ÷ 1 = 8

3. **Multiply** the Ratio by the Multiplier.
   5 × 8 = 40m

   The real Length of the hall is **40m**.

Amounts
8 : 40
Multiplier
× 8   × 8
Scale
1 : 5

× ↑
÷

Exercise 10: 6b   Find the Amount:

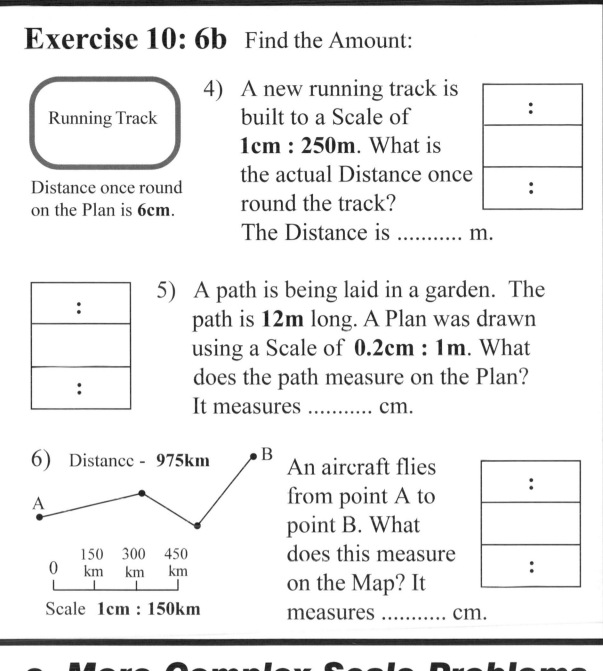

Running Track

Distance once round on the Plan is **6cm**.

4) A new running track is built to a Scale of **1cm : 250m**. What is the actual Distance once round the track? The Distance is .... m.

5) A path is being laid in a garden. The path is **12m** long. A Plan was drawn using a Scale of **0.2cm : 1m**. What does the path measure on the Plan? It measures .... cm.

6) Distance - **975km**

A

B

150 km   300 km   450 km

0

Scale **1cm : 150km**

An aircraft flies from point A to point B. What does this measure on the Map? It measures .... cm.

c. More Complex Scale Problems

Scales sometimes require Conversion from km to cm. Example:

A Map of Wales is drawn to a Scale of **1 : 650,000**. What would a Distance of **130km** be in centimetres on the map?

The Scale is in centimetres. It needs to show **cm** to **km**.

1 cm : 650,~~000~~cm $\longrightarrow$ 1 cm : 6,5~~00~~m

Convert to metres	Convert to kilometres
Divide by **100** (move the Decimal Point two places to the left - **100cm** to **1m**).	Divide by **1000** (Move the Decimal Point three more places to the left).

(For Metric Conversions see **Book 2**)

For speedy conversions it is useful to know there are **100,000cm** in **1km**. In other words move the d.p. 5 places left.

Amounts
? : **130**
Multiplier
?   **?**
Scale
1 : **6.5**

The Scale is **1 cm : 6.5km**

1. Fill out the Ratio Box.

2. **Divide** the Amount by the Scale to find the Multiplier.

   130 ÷ 6.5 = 20

3. **Multiply** the Scale by the the Multiplier.

   1 × 20 = 20

   130km will be
   20cm on the Map.

Amounts
20 : **130**
×20   **×20**
Scale
1 : **6.5**

× ↑ ÷

Exercise 10: 6c Calculate the following:

7) A Map of Great Britain is drawn to a scale of **1 : 800,000**

   What real Distance is represented by **1cm** on the Map?

   Cancel
   ↓
   1 : 800,000

   1 cm = ... km.

8) A Map of Sweden is drawn
to a Scale of **3 : 750,000**

What real Distance is represented
by **1cm** on the Map?

Cancel
↓
3 : 750,000

1 cm = ... km.

9) A Map of Scotland
is drawn to a Scale
of **1 : 300,000**.

Cancel
↓
1 : 300,000

1 cm = ... km.

How would **24km** be represented on
the Map? .... cm.

:
:

10) A Map of Brazil
is drawn to a Scale
of **5 : 400,000**

Cancel
↓
5 : 400,000

1 cm = ... km.

:
:

What real Distance would **10cm** on
the Map represent? .... km.

Score

10. Gradients

Gradient is a way of measuring a Slope. For every
1 unit this slope **Rises** on the **Vertical** plane, it extends
for **5 units** on the **Horizontal** plane.

1 unit

5 units

It can be Expressed as:

A Ratio	**A Percentage**
Vertical Horizontal	• Change the Ratio $\dfrac{1}{\cancel{5}^{1}} \times \dfrac{\cancel{100}^{20}}{1}$
(Rise) (Distance)	to a Fraction
1 : 5	• Multiply by 100% **20%**

75

a. Amount to Gradient

Example:

A forklift truck rises **5m** travelling up a **50m** ramp. What is the Gradient?

Amounts		
Rise		Distance
5	**:**	**50**

1. Find an **HCF** of **50** and **5**. It is **5**.

2. **Cancel** the Amounts (Divide by **5**).

$\div$

Divider	
÷5	**÷5**

3. To **Express as a Percentage**.
   - Change Gradient to Fraction
   - Multiply by **100%**

↓

Gradient	
1	**:**	**10**

$$\frac{1}{{}^1\cancel{10}} \times \frac{\cancel{100}^{\,10}}{1}$$

The **Gradient** is 1 : 10
or **10%**

Exercise 10: 7a   Write the Gradient:

1) A car travels **126 metres** up a hill.
   The Height of the hill is **28 metres**.
   What is the Gradient as a Ratio?

   The Gradient is .... **:** ....

:
:

2) A mountain track Rises **18 metres**
   over a Length of **72 metres**. What is
   the Gradient as a Ratio and Percentage?

   The Gradient is .... **:** .... %

:
:

3) Tom climbs up a steep hill for **160 metres**.
   The Height of the hill is **80 metres**. Write
   the Gradient as a Ratio and Percentage.

   The Gradient is .... **:** .... %

:
:

b. Gradient to Amount

Finding Amounts can involve calculating either the **Rise** or the **Distance** by using the Gradient.

Example: | An athlete runs uphill for **400m**. The Gradient is **1 : 5** (**20%**). What is the Rise?

1. If the Gradient is given as a Percentage, then Convert to a Ratio.
   - Change to a Fraction
   - Simplify/Cancel
   - Express Fraction as a Ratio

$$\frac{\cancel{20}^{\,1}}{\cancel{100}_{\,5}} = \frac{1}{5}$$

1 : 5

Amounts	
Rise	Distance
80 : **400**	

Multiplier
× 80 × 80

Gradient
1 : 5

2. **Divide** the Distance by the Gradient to find the Multiplier.
   400 ÷ 5 = 80

3. **Multiply** the Gradient by the Multiplier.
   1 × 80 = 80

The Rise (Height) is 80m.

Exercise 10: 7b Write the Rise/Distance:

4) A mountaineer climbs uphill for **300m**. The Gradient is **2 : 3**. What is the Rise?

:
:

   The Rise (height) is .... m.

:
:

5) A ski-lift Rises **315m**. The Gradient is **15 : 4**. What Distance does the ski-lift cover?

   The Distance is .... m.

6) A train travels **875km**. The Gradient is **2%**. What is the Rise?

Convert 2% to a Ratio $\dfrac{2}{100} =$

The Rise is .... km.

| : |
| |
| : |

7) A window cleaner climbs a ladder. The Rise is **12m**. The Gradient is **6 : 1**. What Distance does the foot of the ladder measure from the wall of the house?

The Distance is .... m.

| : |
| |
| : |

8) Some climbers ascend a mountain. The Gradient is **15 : 2**. The climbers ascend to a Height of **225m**.

The Distance is .... m.

| : |
| |
| : |

9) Some children ski down a slope. The Distance is **925m**. The Gradient is **8%**. What is the Rise of the slope?

Convert 8% to a Ratio $\dfrac{8}{100} =$

The Rise is .... m.

| : |
| |
| : |

10) Some scouts go on an expedition. They walk a Distance of **48km** at a Gradient of **1 : 6**. What is the Rise?

The Rise is .... km.   **Score** [ ]

| : |
| |
| : |

78

Answers

Maths Book 3

Chapter Nine
Percentages
Exercise 9: 1
1) 42%
2) 24%
3) 48%
4) 45%
5) Shade 32 squares
6) Shade 23 squares
7) Shade 12 squares
8) Shade 55 squares
9) 20%
10) Check yourself

Exercise 9: 2
1) $\frac{6}{25}$
2) $\frac{4}{5}$
3) $\frac{7}{20}$
4) $\frac{19}{20}$
5) $\frac{3}{5}$
6) $\frac{1}{1}$ or 1
7) $\frac{4}{25}$
8) $\frac{2}{5}$
9) $\frac{39}{100}$
10) $\frac{18}{25}$

Exercise 9: 3
1) $1\frac{1}{2}$
2) $3\frac{1}{5}$
3) $3\frac{7}{10}$
4) $\frac{5}{1}$ or 5
5) $2\frac{1}{10}$
6) $1\frac{6}{25}$
7) $3\frac{3}{20}$
8) $6\frac{3}{4}$
9) $1\frac{1}{20}$
10) $4\frac{3}{5}$

Exercise 9: 4
1) $\frac{1}{30}$
2) $\frac{3}{8}$
3) $\frac{2}{3}$
4) $\frac{1}{6}$
5) $\frac{7}{8}$
6) $\frac{1}{16}$
7) $\frac{5}{8}$
8) $\frac{1}{12}$
9) $\frac{5}{6}$
10) $\frac{1}{15}$

Exercise 9: 5
1) 80%
2) 90%
3) 36%
4) 65%
5) 40%
6) 70%
7) 95%
8) 18%
9) 30%
10) 68%

Exercise 9: 6
1) 160%
2) 370%
3) 450%
4) 345%
5) 168%
6) 225%
7) 105%
8) 112%
9) 330%
10) 220%

Exercise 9: 7
1) $31\frac{1}{4}$%
2) $16\frac{2}{3}$%
3) $58\frac{1}{3}$%
4) $87\frac{1}{2}$%
5) $73\frac{1}{3}$%
6) $83\frac{1}{3}$%
7) $6\frac{2}{3}$%
8) $41\frac{2}{3}$%
9) $37\frac{1}{2}$%
10) $93\frac{1}{3}$%

Exercise 9: 8
1) 8
2) 6
3) 170
4) 450
5) 168
6) 7.2g
7) £1.69
8) £11.20
9) 13.5m
10) £5.70

Exercise 9: 9a
1) £2.88
2) £500
3) 21cm
4) 39km
Exercise 9: 9b
5) 663g
6) £262.50
Exercise 9: 9c
7) 8p
8) £5
9) 90cm
10) 15km

Exercise 9: 10a
1) £1.08
2) £32.50
3) 225cm
4) 22km
5) 525m
Exercise 9: 10b
6) 48p
7) £28
8) 78cm
9) 13km
10) 91m

Exercise 9: 11
1) 250
2) 820
3) £240
4) 300km
5) £4.75
6) 260cm
7) 160m
8) £70
9) 350g
10) 60p

Exercise 9: 12a
1) 15%
2) 17%
3) 36%
4) 20%
Exercise 9: 12b
5) 350%
6) 250%

Answers

Exercise 9: 12c

7) $43\frac{3}{4}\%$ 8) $41\frac{2}{3}\%$

9) $37\frac{1}{2}\%$ 10) $83\frac{1}{3}\%$

Exercise 9: 13
1) 62.5% 2) 80%
3) 20% 4) 96.25%
5) 30% 6) 20%
7) 20% 8) 25%
9) 37.5% 10) 85%

Exercise 9: 14
1) £1.82 2) 42cm
3) 45km 4) £2.61
5) £1.54 6) 950km
7) 36% 8) 12.5%
9) 37.5% 10) 25%

Exercise 9: 15a
1) £120 2) £2,500
3) £15 4) £3,375
5) £200

Exercise 9: 15b
6) 16% 7) 20%
8) 40% 9) 18%
10) 25%

Exercise 9: 16a
1) £305.50 2) £468

Exercise 9: 16b
3) £80 4) £160
5) £137.50

Exercise 9: 16c
6) £360 7) £342
8) 14.5% 9) £44
10) £11

Exercise 9: 17
1) 150 marks 2) £78
3) £2.47 4) 70%
5) a) £12 b) £2.50
   c) £14 d) £8
6) a) 25% b) 37.5%
7) a) 2$\dot{1}$7 hens b) 140 pigs
8) 41.$\dot{6}$% or $41\frac{2}{3}\%$
9) £9.20 10) £305.50

Exercise 9: 18a
1) 0.14 2) 0.54
3) 0.99 4) 1.5
5) 0.56

Exercise 9: 18b
6) 94% 7) 125%
8) 5% 9) 265%
       10) 11%

Exercise 9: 19
1) £20.40 2) 18.2km
3) £35.84 4) 2.4cm
5) 54 litres 6) 180m
7) 30p 8) 3m
9) 561km 10) 7.5p

Exercise 9: 20
1) 37.5% 2) 35%
3) 40% 4) 4%
5) 62.5% 6) 13.$\dot{3}$%
7) 65% 8) 15%
9) 2.5% 10) 33.$\dot{3}$%

Exercise 9: 21
1) $\frac{1}{3}$ 0.$\dot{3}$ 33.$\dot{3}$%

2) $\frac{19}{20}$ 0.95 95%

3) $\frac{1}{5}$ 0.2 20%

4) $\frac{2}{5}$ 0.4 40%

5) $\frac{1}{4}$ 0.25 25%

6) $\frac{9}{10}$ 0.9 90%

7) $\frac{1}{8}$ 0.125 12.5%

8) $\frac{4}{5}$ 0.8 80%

9) $\frac{5}{8}$ 0.625 62.5%

10) $\frac{1}{3}$ 0.$\dot{3}$ 33.$\dot{3}$%

Exercise 9: 22
1) 0.02 $\frac{3}{100}$ 4%

2) 9% 0.08 $\frac{1}{13}$

3) 2% 4) 12%

5) 4% 6) 0.03

7) 5% 8) $\frac{1}{12}$

9) 0.04 10) 0.1

Exercise 9: 23
1) 0.0213 2) 0.036
3) 0.007 4) 0.0989
5) 0.018 6) 0.105
7) 33.4% 8) 6.9%
9) 81.2% 10) 136.7%

Exercise 9: 24
1) 2.15% 2) 0.07
3) $\frac{1}{20}$ 4) 1.95%
5) 4.16% 6) $\frac{1}{12}$

7) 0.07 8) 0.1

9) 0.02 2.1% $\frac{3}{100}$

10) 9.1% 0.08 $\frac{1}{13}$

Answers

Maths Book 3

Chapter Ten
Ratio and Proportion
Exercise 10: 1a

1a) $4 : 5$ and $\frac{4}{9}$ to $\frac{5}{9}$

 b) $4 : 7$ and $\frac{4}{11}$ to $\frac{7}{11}$

2a) $11 : 5 : 3$ and
      $\frac{11}{19}$ to $\frac{5}{19}$ to $\frac{3}{19}$

 b) $3 : 4$ and $\frac{3}{7}$ to $\frac{4}{7}$

Exercise 10: 1b

3a) $1 : 1.5$ or $1 : 1\frac{1}{2}$

 b) $1 : 1.25$ or $1 : 1\frac{1}{4}$

4a) $1 : 3.5$ or $1 : 3\frac{1}{2}$

 b) $1 : 2.25$ or $1 : 2\frac{1}{4}$

5a) $1 : 1.\dot{6}$ or $1 : 1\frac{2}{3}$

 b) $1 : 2$

6a) $1 : 1.5$ or $1 : 1\frac{1}{2}$

 b) $1 : 1.25$ or $1 : 1\frac{1}{4}$

7a) $1 : 3.5$ or $1 : 3\frac{1}{2}$

 b) $1 : 4.5$ or $1 : 4\frac{1}{2}$

Exercise 10: 1c
8a) $4 : 5$ b) $\frac{6}{7}$

Exercise 10: 1d
9a) 75 %   b) 45 %

Exercise 10: 1e
10a) $13 : 20$ b) $9 : 10$

Exercise 10: 2

1) $20 : 7$ and $\frac{20}{27}$ to $\frac{7}{27}$

2) $3 : 7$ and $\frac{3}{10}$ to $\frac{7}{10}$

3) $1 : 4$ and $\frac{1}{5}$ to $\frac{4}{5}$

4) $1 : 3$ and $\frac{1}{4}$ to $\frac{3}{4}$

5) $2 : 3$ and $\frac{2}{5}$ to $\frac{3}{5}$

6) $2 : 1$ and $\frac{2}{3}$ to $\frac{1}{3}$

7) $10 : 3 : 2$ 8) $3 : 2$

9) $4 : 3 : 2$ 10) $3 : 1 : 5$

Exercise 10: 3
1) $7 : 4$ 2) $10 : 1$
3) $15 : 1$ 4) $2 : 25$
5) $1 : 7$ 6) $1 : 20$
7) $4 : 3 : 2$ 8) $5 : 1$
9) $1 : 4$ 10) $7 : 3$

Exercise 10: 4a
1)   £50 : £70
2)   3m : 6m : 9m
Exercise 10: 4b
3)   25 pencils
4)   15 stickers
5)   12 girls
Exercise 10: 4c
6)   15 wet days
7)   3 yoyos
Exercise 10: 4d
8)   72 : 36 : 9 years
9)   36 : 18 : 6 minutes
10) 72 : 24 : 8 sweets

Exercise 10: 5a
1) 4 hours
2) 30 days
Exercise 10: 5b
3) Vidhur has £6.50
    Anne has £4.10
4) smaller is 180
    bigger is 240
5) smaller is 40cm
    bigger is 90cm

Exercise 10: 5c
6) John has £210
    Alex has £255
    Dean has £195
7) Ravi has 240
    Daniel has 204
    Premdeep has 156
Exercise 10: 5d
8) a) Andrew has least
    b) Keshav has most
    c) He gives 4 to James
    d) He gives 8 to Andrew
9) a) £1.20 b) £1.30
Exercise 10: 5e
10) a) At the finish Paul has
      144; John has 72 and
      Don has 36
    b) At the start Paul has
      150; John has 62 and
      Don has 40

Exercise 10: 6a
1) $1 : 9$ 2) $1 : 3$
3) $1 : 20$
Exercise 10: 6b
4) 1500m 5) 2. 4cm
6) 6.5cm
Exercise 10: 6c
7) 8km   8) 2.5km
9) 8cm   10) 8km

Exercise 10: 7a
1) $2 : 9$
2) $1 : 4$ and 25%
3) $1 : 2$ and 50%
Exercise 10: 7b
4) 200m   5) 84m
6) 17.5km   7) 2m
8) 30m   9) 74m
10) 8km

PROGRESS CHARTS

9. PERCENTAGES

Scores

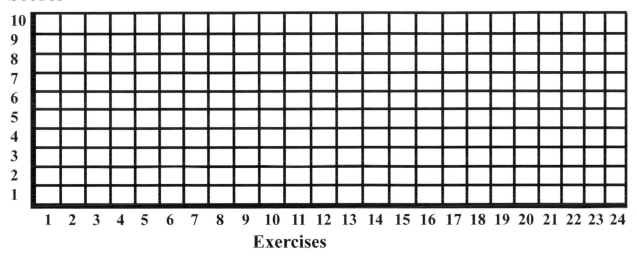

Exercises

Total Score

Percentage

%

---

10. RATIO AND PROPORTION

Scores

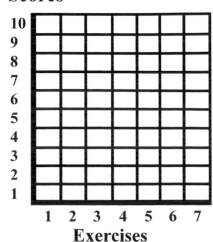

Exercises

Total Score

Percentage

%

For the average add up % and divide by 2

Overall Percentage

%

CERTIFICATE
OF
ACHIEVEMENT
(Third)

This certifies................................ has completed **Maths Book Three** successfully.

Overall Percentage Score Achieved.

%

Comment...................................
....

Signed ....
(teacher/parent/guardian)

Date ....